THE REI

THE
RED BOOK
THE HANRAHAN CASE AGAINST MERCK, SHARP AND DOHME

Jerry O'Callaghan

POOLBEG

For Joan, Denis, Dermot, Sarah and Maeve,
and for my mother, Yanna.

A Paperback Original
First published 1992 by
Poolbeg Press Ltd
Knocksedan House
Swords, Co. Dublin, Ireland
Reprinted January 1992

© Jerry O'Callaghan, 1992
The moral right of the author has been asserted

ISBN 1 85371 208 6

Cover design by Pomphrey Associates
Set by Richard Parfrey in ITC Stone Serif 9.5/12
Printed by The Guernsey Press Company Ltd,
Vale, Guernsey, Channel Islands

CONTENTS

ACKNOWLEDGEMENTS

This book arose from the ordeal of the Hanrahan family, and I hope it can make some small amends for that ordeal by telling the story. I cannot thank them adequately for the time and attention they gave relating it to me. My thanks are due also to many of their neighbours, advisers and consultants, too numerous to mention by name, who filled in the story around them.

The book is based mainly on the High Court and Supreme Court transcripts and on more than a dozen reports by state and semi-state agencies on the case. Much of that material I accumulated while doing research for an RTE programme on the subject which was eventually broadcast on "Today Tonight" in November 1988. I wish to thank my colleagues in RTE for their help and encouragement throughout, in particular Cian Ó hÉigeartaigh. the programme producer, Liam O'Flanagan, who read the first draft and suggested valuable amendments, and Shay Howell for his advice and for directing me to Poolbeg.

I wish to thank Jo O'Donoghue and Philip MacDermott of Poolbeg for their guidance but especially for their patience in awaiting the outcome. Special thanks are due to the editor, Séamas Ó Brógáin, for whipping the manuscript into shape.

However, the final effort here is my own and neither the Hanrahans, RTE nor any of the people mentioned should be blamed for whatever its shortcomings may be.

Finally, I must thank my sister Kate and her husband Patrick for indulging me and this project over two hot summers in New York, and my family for tolerating my anti-social behaviour during the many hours I spent writing the book.

FOREWORD

BY JOHN HANRAHAN

One of my earliest memories in Ballycurkeen is waking to the hollow ring of empty milk cans bumping around in the yard, then the sound of milk pouring into them and the clatter of galvanised buckets. Before I got up the milking would be finished and the milk gone off to the creamery. When I got older I had the job of driving the cows back to the fields after milking on my way to school, the sheepdog barking along with me as far as the bounds ditch. Later I began to do all that myself, starting at 5.30 a.m. and finishing before many of my neighbours got up.

So it hurt to be branded a bad farmer and to see it written in a civil servant's report in 1982 that my farm was overstocked and short of fertiliser and that my cattle were dying of hunger and neglect. It hurt because as far back as I can remember we had the name of being top-class farmers in the area. Even in 1981, at the height of our trouble, the chief agricultural officer brought a group of French people to see how a well-managed Irish farm was run.

But there are worse things you can be called than a bad farmer, and I was called a few choice names. They said I was always in court, that I was a drunk, a crank, a lunatic, that I saw my chance to get easy money from a multinational company. We knew they must have been desperate for a defence to have to resort to those tactics.

In fact I had only stood in court once before in my life, when I was called as a stand-by witness to a road accident. Maybe once a week I take a glass of wine with a meal or an odd drink with friends. A crank I certainly was. There was no other choice: it was either complain or go under. I'll leave it to others to judge whether I'm a lunatic, but I know there were times during the last ten years when my sanity was threatened. I would sometimes lie awake at night listening to the cattle moaning and wondering if I was having a nightmare. But when I got up in the morning the nightmare continued. I was faced with another dead animal, or a sick child, or the whiff of acid on the wind. Our own vets and advisers could see for themselves what was happening; but nobody in authority, nobody who could do anything to stop it, would believe us. As for easy money! All the money in Merck wouldn't compensate us for the destruction of our herd and the years of lost health and peace of mind. Anyway, we had money enough. All we wanted was clean air.

During the past ten years, as our case became more and more public, I was generally the focus of media attention, even the target of abuse; but it was my family who were suffering the most. My wife, Selina, found herself in the prime of life suddenly faced with ill health and upset and trying to protect the children. I want to pay her a very special tribute. I could not have continued without her. At the same time she had to run the farm with me and often keep the accounts from her hospital bed. My mother had to watch our farm almost ruined, the model farm she had built up over fifty years with my aunt. I have them to thank, but there are many others we have to thank together for standing by us when it wasn't popular to do so.

Without our vet and long-time family friend Tom de Lacy we had no chance. No matter what time of the day or night we called him he came out, and indeed it wasn't for the money: he only charged for half the calls, not to mention the time and money he spent travelling to meetings all over the country to fight our case. But the most important thing he did was to believe in us.

Tom's partner and son-in-law, Ger Clancy, arrived in South Tipperary long after our problems began and could have done without the hostility our case brought to those involved. But he never took that view, and fought our battle to the end. Nor can we thank enough Martin O'Gorman and Eddie Keating, the two other vets with Tom de Lacy. They had their own careers to look after and could have left our problems to others. And speaking of vets, I have to thank Peter Dougan for not stopping to think of what he had to lose when he told the simple truth.

Pat Quinlan was always on hand to look after the farm at Ballycurkeen, especially when we were unable to be there, and we could not have fought the case without him. Our neighbour Tommy Rockett knew very well what was happening to us, because it was happening to his own animals on a smaller scale. He could have let us fight our own case, as others did; but whether we needed practical, financial or moral support, he was ready to provide it. Also on hand to support us were neighbours like John Callanan, John Wallace, Johnny Widger, Ray Foley, and Noel Perigoe.

Gone to his reward elsewhere is Dave Hurley, former chief agricultural officer of South Tipperary, who wanted to testify in court in a wheelchair. Still giving his support is Michael English, the man who took over that job. It was always comforting to know that Michael and his farm advisory staff were behind us, because they would have known if farm management was at fault.

Needless to say we could not have fought the case without our solicitor, Tom Menton of O'Keeffe and Lynch. He and the barristers—Tom Smyth, Dermot Gleeson, and Dan Herbert—stuck with us when they knew that if we lost there was no chance of getting paid.

If it hadn't been for Drs Paul and Valerie Dowding of Trinity College, Dublin, I believe our case would have sunk under the weight of science and technology; they had the ability and courage to take on the establishment. Our thanks are also due to Dr Geoffrey Buck, Dr Rory Finegan, Dr Louis Gleeson and Dr James Neufeld, who brought their experience of other cases, and Dr Bill Murray of Cork Regional Technical College, now no longer with us. In the scientific category also I thank Professor Muiris Fitzgerald for his crucial evidence and his advice when it was needed. Finally I must thank everyone else who testified for us when they didn't have to and when there was no reward for it. For all these people this book puts our case on record and their contribution to it.

I first met Jerry O'Callaghan on the street in Clonmel

on a fine day in early June 1984. He had been to the farm and talked to Selina and my mother, who told him where to find me. It was obvious from the start that he had a grasp of farming knowledge not usually found in a journalist; I knew he understood right away that bad farm management was not our problem, whatever else it was. Over the years he has kept faith and shown the tenacity required to get to grips with the complex issues of this case and put them across in a way that the ordinary reader can understand.

Finally I want to say to the people who work in the Merck, Sharp and Dohme factory that I bear them no ill will, whatever they think about me. I was happy to see the factory arrive in South Tipperary, and so were my family, because as far as I was concerned they were neighbours and I was glad to be of service. Our attitude was that jobs were badly needed in the area and we would all be better off as a result.

We never wanted to see the plant closed. I know the importance of a job and a livelihood. After all, my own livelihood was seriously threatened. So was my life and that of my family, however dramatic that may sound. I saw our cattle dying at an alarming rate, our dogs, our ponies and our pets sick and dying in the same way. We had the same symptoms and sickness ourselves. It was obvious to anybody who spent any time on the farm that something was poisoning us.

We looked around to see where that poison might be coming from, and we didn't have far to look. Only a mile down the road was enough poison to wipe out half the countryside if it happened to be getting out. That it does no apparent harm to the people who work in the middle of it is a tribute to the company's competence and control in dealing with it. As to how it should have got to our farm in Ballycurkeen, I don't know exactly, but this book is the best attempt at grappling with that mystery that you are likely to find.

I only ask you to read it.

1

CASE DISMISSED

"It is all too clear that Mr John Hanrahan's belief that the troubles he was experiencing were in some way associated with the processes carried on in the factory developed into something of an obsession, which can only have diverted his time and energies away from the very real problems he was facing on the farm."

It was approaching 1.00 p.m. on Wednesday 7 August 1985, and Mr Justice Ronan Keane had been reading his judgement for two hours. John Hanrahan sat welded to the hard benches of courtroom number 1 in the Four Courts, Dublin, a place he had come to know well. Earlier that year he had sat there for forty-seven days with his wife, Selina, and his mother, Mary, during their High Court hearing against Merck, Sharp and Dohme, the longest civil case in Irish legal history.

Hanrahan believed that emissions from the Merck, Sharp and Dohme chemical plant near his farm in Ballycurkeen, Carrick-on-Suir, Co Tipperary, had killed 140 of his cattle, damaged his health and that of his family, and brought him to the brink of desperation. He knew that had this belief not developed into something of an obsession he would not have pursued it so relentlessly to this conclusion. But the judge believed that the obsession was the cause, not the result, of his problems.

"The plaintiffs have, accordingly, wholly failed to discharge the onus of proof upon them of establishing that

1

the injury to health, animal and plant life of which they complain was caused by emissions from the defendants' factory . . . It follows that the plaintiffs' claim must be dismissed."

Across the courtroom aisle the Merck team were jubilant. The company had defended the case every inch of the way. Through the forty-seven days they had challenged every accusation, countered each of the Hanrahans' witnesses, and produced an array of experts from Ireland, Britain and the United States to offer reasons other than factory emissions for each complaint.

Merck's defence strategy was to concentrate on what it presented as John Hanrahan's shortcomings as a farmer. It freely admitted that at times unpleasant odours were emitted from the chemical plant but argued that these remained within permitted levels. Furthermore, none of the scientific studies carried out had found any direct link between factory emissions and the farm problems. On the other hand they argued that each of the phenomena described could be attributed to bad farm management. Hanrahan had too little experience of dairy farming and became so paranoid about the factory that he neglected his business. Mr Justice Keane accepted that defence.

The Hanrahans shuffled out of the court and made their way outside to a battery of reporters. How did they feel? What would they do now? How would they pay the costs? Would they have to sell out? John Hanrahan said something about an appeal before driving away.

The truth was that the prospect of mounting an appeal was remote. In fact the Hanrahans were facing ruin. Their legal costs were approaching £1 million, and Merck's costs, for which they would now be liable, would stretch well beyond that figure. They owed £100,000 to Avonmore Co-op and £200,000 to the bank. During the hearing their farm had been valued at £580,000. Including cattle and machinery, they had assets of about £700,000. They owed more than three times what they were worth.

Their legal team was advising appeal, but before this

could even be considered some legal fees at least would have to be paid. They were trapped. There was no alternative but to sell.

The family could have sold at the first sign of trouble and moved to another farm. But another farm was not what they wanted. "Why should we have left?" Mary Hanrahan asked. "We were here before them." Mary was a descendant of Sir Phillip de Mandeville, who received from King Henry II a grant of land between Carrick-on-Suir and Clonmel, on which he built Ballydine Castle, the home of the Mandevilles for six hundred years. The Ballydine land was lost and regained a number of times in the late eighteenth and early nineteenth centuries; eventually, in a rare twist of irony, Merck, Sharp and Dohme bought it for their chemical factory in 1972.

Other branches of the family owned the farm at Ballycurkeen, just over a mile from Ballydine, as well as land in Waterford, Clonmel, and Mitchelstown. In 1887 the owner of the Mitchelstown land, John Mandeville—a nephew of the Young Irelander and Fenian John O'Mahony —was imprisoned for Land League activities, suffering ill health as a result, from which he died soon after his release.

In 1912 Mary Hanrahan's mother, Lillian, a niece of John Mandeville, left her home in Mitchelstown to marry William Quaid in Newcastlewest, Co Limerick. In 1936, at the age of eighteen, it was Mary Quaid's turn to leave home. With her younger sister, Wilhemena, she went to live with their uncle James in Ballycurkeen, where she began to run the farm after he died in 1940. There was a work force of six men in those days, and all cultivation was done by horses, but her stewardship coincided with the Second World War and the introduction of compulsory tillage. Mary found horses too slow to cope with the extra work, and she bought an iron-wheeled tractor and trailing plough. She drove the tractor and plough all the way from Kanturk to Ballycurkeen, a distance of eighty miles, taking two days for the journey. It was one of the first tractors in South Tipperary, and Mary did the ploughing herself.

In 1942 she married John Hanrahan senior, and they moved to a bungalow on the farm, as another uncle, Frank, was by then living in the main dwelling, Ballycurkeen House, a splendid eighteenth-century building with eighteen rooms. Mary and John had four children: Frances, Judy, Dolly, and John. After the uncle died they moved to the big house; they sold the bungalow and 70 acres to pay death duties but were left with 265 acres of the best Suir valley land, a sizable holding by Irish standards.

John Hanrahan was interested in drystock, and ran a beef cattle and sheep system. But Mary began to milk dairy cows in the early nineteen-fifties, when few farmers had realised their potential. Over the years she established a reputation as a strong, capable woman of solid integrity.

In the mid-fifties Dave Hurley, the chief agricultural officer for South Tipperary, drew up a seven-year plan for the farm, and began a professional and personal relationship with the family that was to last until his death in 1985. They gradually increased the dairy herd numbers, and to generate cash they grew seed wheat for the Department of Agriculture. John Hanrahan died in 1968, but by then Mary was already running the farm with her family and Wilhemena. "We were prospering. Things were working very well. Our dairy herd was getting bigger and bigger. We became the largest milk suppliers at our creamery."

They built a milking parlour, and were one of the first to start making silage in the fifties. Ballycurkeen became a model farm, and the agricultural advisory service under Dave Hurley used it regularly for demonstrations. Mary continued to own the farm throughout the traumatic affair with Merck, Sharp and Dohme.

John Hanrahan junior was born in 1948 and began full-time farming after secondary school. He developed a keen interest in machinery, but also looked after the calves and the livestock breeding programme. In 1969 he married Selina Lavelle, who grew up in a farming area just across the Suir in Co Waterford. Her family was not in farming but she was no stranger to the life and got involved in all aspects of the farm as soon as she moved to Ballycurkeen. They had two sons, Charles, born in 1970, and Ambrose, born in 1972.

It was in 1978 when Dolly left to get married and Mary had in effect retired that John took over the management of the farm. By then they were milking a hundred cows, rearing all calves to the beef stage, and doing some tillage. Dairy farming was now at the crest of a wave, and John decided to concentrate entirely on this and phase out the beef and tillage. With his advisers he drew up an ambitious plan to double milking cow numbers and carry young calves and replacement heifers for the dairy herd instead of the beef cattle. It meant he had to borrow to make improvements, but the prevailing wisdom was that investment in dairy farming was the right decision. That advice was dramatically justified when the introduction five years later of milk quotas put a stop to any further investment in milking cows.

On 15 August 1985, the week following Mr Justice Keane's High Court verdict, John Hanrahan met the chairman and regional manager of Avonmore Co-op, his milk buyer and feed supplier. Though he was fully secured, they told him they had decided to withhold half his monthly milk cheque to offset against his outstanding account. The family's income was cut in half at the stroke of a pen, and shortly they would face another winter with a herd of 350 animals and no money to buy feed for them. But worse, it put paid to any possibility of appealing the High Court decision.

There seemed to be only one choice. When the Avonmore cheque arrived a few days later, the Hanrahans gave instructions to their solicitor to advertise the farm.

The auction was a sober affair. It was held in the Dublin offices of Hamilton and Hamilton on 12 September. A number of potential buyers had been to view the farm, but few showed up on the day, and no more than three or four of them could have put together the kind of money needed. But apart from the chemical poisoning issue, a serious impediment was the involuntary nature of the sale. Whatever the attitude to the Hanrahans' case it was common knowledge that the farm was not being sold by choice, and the history of land tenure has developed in Irish farmers an automatic solidarity in the face of such events. Anyone who assisted a forced sale by offering market value would be less than popular with his neighbours.

Despite the pressure from so many sources the Hanrahans had resolved that the farm would not be sold cheap and had set a reserve price that reflected its true value, ignoring the circumstances of the sale. Early bidding lacked any serious intent, and after further prompting it stopped at a half-hearted £360,000. No sale.

But although they were safe for the moment their problems remained. It had been decided that the stock would have to go, and another auction was set for 25 September on the farm.

"I couldn't really describe my feelings," Mary Hanrahan told reporters on the day of the auction. "I feel very bitter, very sore about it."

"But are you packing, ready to leave?"

"Well, I won't go too easy, I'll tell you. I won't walk out with my hands in my pockets and say day-day. My family were here, I had visions of my grandsons and their grandsons continuing on. I won't go out without being pushed out."

"But is the fight not over, in as much as the farm is for sale?"

"Oh, no, the fight isn't over. The farm, the courts and all that have gone against us, but the fight is by no means over."

In the gathering crowd the tall, spare figure of John Hanrahan moved from one group to another, grim and unsmiling, exchanging brief comments with interested buyers and speaking briefly for television. "Last week I had to get a loan of the money for the wages to pay the men, which gave me time to give them at least a week's notice. Some of those men are here twenty-five years. My wife got no money for shopping—that's the position. I can't sleep at night-time, I see my wife can't sleep, my kids crying going to bed. That's more that any man can take."

The prices offered were disappointing. But over two-thirds of the animals were sold, along with some machinery. The proceeds were approximately £90,000, enough to enable the appeal procedure to begin and allow Hanrahan to continue farming. He was left eventually with just over a hundred animals, including fifty-seven milking cows.

A few days after the auction Hanrahan was told by his bank that they could honour no more cheques. They asked for proposals for settling his outstanding account of £200,000, and for an immediate lodgement of £20,000. He said he had no money to give them. He was asked to explain his refusal to sell the farm and to lodge the money from the stock auction—not an unreasonable request in the circumstances. He simply outlined his legal position and explained that no appeal would be possible without the auction money, and no settlement of accounts would be possible without the appeal.

Relations with Avonmore had deteriorated; and Hanrahan could not transfer his milk to another buyer because of a Department of Agriculture rule requiring three months' notice. But he did find another buyer, and gave notice to Avonmore at the end of September. In the meantime the milk of the remaining cows continued to go to Avonmore until the end of the year, but without any payment: the £22,000 for milk supplied before the end of December went towards reducing the outstanding feed bill.

There was one further confrontation. A week after the notice of transfer was handed in, Hanrahan sent a tractor and trailer to the co-op for a load of cattle feed. It was refused. For thirty years the family had dealt with the co-op, on the usual credit terms. The circumstances now were somewhat different; but Hanrahan was determined that his trauma would continue to be played out in public. He sent for the feed again the following day, and went along himself to protest at the refusal. This time the media were on hand to record the incident.

That afternoon cow 278, heavy in calf, collapsed on the lawn in front of the house and began to bleed heavily. Hanrahan called the vet, who was unable to save the cow or calf but decided to do a post-mortem examination. With the media standing by again he found evidence of heart trouble and massive internal bleeding, a phenomenon that came as no surprise to Hanrahan or his vet. It fitted into a pattern of events that began at Ballycurkeen early one morning in August 1978.

2

THE TROUBLE BEGINS

John Hanrahan woke at his usual time of 5.15 a.m. on Sunday 27 August 1978. He knew it was calm and overcast, perhaps misty, outside. There was no hint of light from the east window, and he could hear a characteristic muffled coughing from the animals. By 1978 such coughing was commonplace on mornings like this.

He left the house in darkness, switched on the outside light, and made his way towards the cattle sheds. Entering the yard he felt a stinging sensation in his face and a shortening of breath that threatened to overpower him. Beneath the floodlight a swirling brownish fog caught his attention. "I felt it in my eyes and the exposed parts of my skin, and I saw it when I looked up towards the light . . . As soon as I discovered the burning of my eyes and skin I went back to the house and phoned Merck, Sharp and Dohme."

As he waited in the old hallway he noticed the windows vibrating as they would from a passing train, the same drumming sensation he got through the pillow on still nights when the Merck incinerator was operating. He got through to someone he thought was a security man. He asked him if they would switch off what they were letting out; it wasn't possible to milk the cows. They said they would look into it.

He went back out again, and discovered that the cattle nearest to the milking parlour had a discharge coming from their eyes. The first batch of cows had already assembled in the collecting yard adjoining the milking parlour, and he could see that the whole herd was affected. The eye discharge was running down their faces. He ran to the phone again and this time spoke to his vet, Tom de Lacy, describing in detail the brown fog, the burning sensation, the coughing, the running eyes and noses.

It was nearly daylight when Hanrahan arrived outside for the ʳd time that mᵒʳning, and the brown haze seemed to have lifted. A neighbour who worked at Merck got out of a car and approached him, asking what the problem was. Hanrahan said he wanted to see someone in higher authority, someone who knew about chemicals.

Tom de Lacy arrived before nine, a big man in his sixties who had known the farm for almost forty years. By 1978 he was a family friend and knew he would not have been called on Sunday morning unless the problem was serious. He found the animals still coughing, weeping, and running from the nose.

From 1977 de Lacy had noticed a certain deterioration in the health of the Hanrahan herd. Respiratory problems were commoner and calves were "inclined to be sleepy" and unwilling to take their feed. There were more calf deaths than before, and some deformities. The adult animals were sometimes uneasy and stampeding in the yards. But this kind of widespread distress could only be due to some kind of irritant. There was nothing he could do.

The following day Merck's personnel manager invited John and Mary Hanrahan to visit the factory to discuss their experience. "We told them what had happened . . . They promised it would never happen to us again. They would look into the whole matter and we could go home and they would see that everything was done to prevent anything like it happening."

Selina Hanrahan had her first signs of ill health in 1976, six months after the Merck factory began operations. She was admitted to hospital in Waterford on 6 September 1976 with uterine bleeding. At the time she did not blame the factory for her problem, but in the light of subsequent developments she came to feel it was responsible. She spent a week in hospital that September and enjoyed reasonable health for a while on her return home; but towards the end of 1977 a feeling of nausea and weakness began to develop, and she suffered increasingly from chest pains, sore throat and nose, and weeping eyes. When she woke in the morning the pillow would be wet from overnight weeping. Iron injections for anaemia were prescribed, to no avail.

After the first encounter with Merck in August 1978 the more obvious symptoms continued. There were intermittent smells, irritation of eyes, nose, and throat, weakness, tiredness, pains at the back of the eyes, and chest pains. They complained repeatedly to Merck and to South Tipperary County Council. About this time also they began to blame a gradually increasing number of calf deaths on the factory.

The Hanrahans were not alone in their plight. Other neighbours had also begun to complain, and in 1979 Merck set up a procedure to deal with them. When a complaint was made it was logged, and someone was sent to investigate, both outside and inside the plant. Some complaints came from workers inside the plant; but the more usual pattern was for odour complaints to be recorded from local people when nothing had been reported by the workers. It made it more difficult for neighbours to convince Merck that their complaints were genuine.

At 9.45 a.m. on 26 May 1979 Ray Foley rang the factory to say that he found a sweetish choking smell around his farmyard. His land adjoins the Merck premises and his farmyard is 300 yards due east of the nearest emission source. He said he had detected the same smell several times already during that week. One of the Merck staff checked the perimeter fences but found nothing, and when he called to Foley at 10.00 a.m. the smell was no longer detectable. A review of production operations logged along with the complaint showed that there should have been no venting at the time. This was a fairly typical incident, which would help to explain how Merck personnel developed a somewhat sceptical attitude. Of thirty-eight odour complaints recorded from eight different neighbours in 1979, only one was confirmed by Merck staff on visiting the site of the complaint. Yet in one of those complaints, from a nearby pub early in 1980, the record showed that seven customers had left because of the smell.

But some complaints did get a response. On the afternoon of Wednesday 8 August 1979 John Hanrahan rang the factory to complain of a foul odour at his farm. He spoke to Frank Wyatt, head of engineering. He was told that during the holiday period some waste treatment tank was inactive, and that whatever was left of it had gone wrong. "He was a little bit hot and bothered about it. I was informed by Mr Wyatt I would have to put up with it. It would take a number of hours before it would be rectified."

Hanrahan complained to the county council at the same time and got a letter some days later from an official admitting that he himself had detected the odour when he called to the plant. He gave the same reason for the odour as Wyatt, and explained how occasional malfunctions of equipment or human error could occur at the plant but that these were kept to a minimum.

Merck's log showed no complaint from the Hanrahans in August 1979.

By 1980 most of the Hanrahan family were feeling unwell. John made repeated visits to his GP, Dr Anthony Roche-Nagle, and to the county medical officer, Dr AN de Souza. He suffered tightness and pain in his chest, wheezing, coughing, headache, nausea, irritation of his eyes, nose, and throat, and burning of his face and hands. Neither doctor could find his general health affected, but at the end of March 1980 a Dublin chest specialist, Professor Muiris Fitzgerald, diagnosed a condition he described as airway obstruction or reduced pulmonary function. Results of blood and allergy tests were normal, and there was no evidence of asthma. Professor Fitzgerald wrote to Dr Roche-Nagle:

"There is very strong circumstantial evidence to suggest that his respiratory state is due to or, at least, greatly aggravated by airborne fumes or vapours discharged from a nearby manufacturing plant. I am seriously concerned that Mr Hanrahan's respiratory condition may deteriorate if he continues to be exposed to noxious materials. Undoubtedly, it must present a significant hazard to other people in the neighbourhood."

Mary Hanrahan was also having chest pains. After she retired from farming in 1978 she took up gardening and would spend hours at a time in the garden in front of the house, usually early in the morning. She began to notice "horrible smells—very, very bad smells." Some mornings everything would be fine, but on other mornings she had to leave the garden because of the pains. She would be unable to work for the rest of the day, and on many occasions got such a bad pain that she had to go to bed.

□

Rows of encircling trees interrupt a direct view of the Merck factory from most parts of the Hanrahans' farmyard. The same trees and a road separate the farmyard from the adjacent farm to the south, owned by the Hanrahans' nearest neighbour, Tommy Rockett. Much of Rockett's farmyard is also hidden by trees, but part of a large cattle shed juts out into the prevailing south-west wind blowing up the valley from Merck. Rockett described how the paint had been stripped off the unsheltered part of the corrugated iron roof of the shed; at the same time metal corrosion was evident at Hanrahan's farm on sheds and gates facing the factory. In January 1980 Merck installed a monitor at the farm in an attempt to identify the source of corrosion. It was left in place for six weeks, but nothing conclusive was reported.

By March 1980 gathering protests from residents persuaded the county council to undertake air quality measurements, and they commissioned An Foras Forbartha to carry out the tests. An environmental chemist, Dr Ian Jamieson, arrived to begin the study on 27 March 1980. On 15 May he installed monitors at two sites on the factory premises, on Hanrahan's farm and Foley's farm, and at Noel Perigoe's public house, just across the road from the factory. The monitors measured the level of acid and organic chemicals in the air at these five sites over an eight-week period.

Jamieson's report, in October 1980, concluded that the odour was due to thioanisole—a foul-smelling volatile liquid that occurs as an impurity in one of the ingredients of sulindac, an anti-arthritic drug manufactured by Merck. The report said that repeated releases of thioanisole were unacceptable, but harmless. Average acid levels were well below those recorded in Dublin at the same time of year and were well within accepted health standards. However, acid concentrations were three times higher at Hanrahan's farm than at Foley's, and calculations showed that relatively high concentrations might occur at Hanrahan's farm for short periods. Corrosion on Hanrahan's farm was reported as normal for rural areas, and further monitoring of the air and factory emissions was recommended.

Jamieson's findings failed to satisfy the residents, and in December a group met some county council members and officials to discuss the report. They pressed for the further monitoring Jamieson had recommended, and asked whether Merck could be forced to stop releasing thioanisole.

A further meeting was held in the county council chamber in Clonmel in February 1981. It was attended by officials of the agricultural advisory service and the Department of Agriculture, a representative of the IFA, Dr Jamieson, and Tom de Lacy, as well as a dozen residents, including John and Mary Hanrahan and their solicitor. A decision was taken to set up a technical group to investigate the problem and make recommendations. Included would be Dr Jamieson and personnel from the Department of Agriculture, the universities and An Foras Talúntais (now "Teagasc") as required. This group never met; but the council was prevailed on to commission a further study of air quality from An Foras Forbartha. On 15 April Dr Jamieson set up monitors at three locations on Hanrahan's farm and one at Perigoe's pub to take continuous measurements of acid and organic levels in the air. It was to be a more elaborate and longer-lasting study than the previous one.

But events were soon overtaken by developments on Hanrahan's farm.

3

BACKGROUND

From the nineteen-sixties successive Governments have operated an "open-door" policy for attracting foreign companies to Ireland, and through this open door have come a myriad of US and other multinationals eager to avail of the Irish tax haven and cheap labour. When Ireland joined the EC in 1973 it became an easy conduit to Europe for these companies; as a bonus they got generous capital grants and tax concessions. Typically the raw materials for these industries are imported from the parent company and processed in Ireland, and the product is then exported tax-free to other European countries. By the middle of the nineteen-eighties more than 80 per cent of Irish exports other than food came from subsidiaries of multinational companies.

The valley of the River Suir is probably the richest farmland in Ireland, green and fertile, with big and prosperous farms. But although farming and food-processing prospered, the towns of Clonmel and Carrick-on-Suir were unemployment black-spots. Against this background South Tipperary Development Association (STDA) was set up, in co-operation with the county council, to attract industry to the area. The first to show real interest was the American-owned Merck and Company, a pharmaceutical multi-national based in New Jersey.

The county manager and county engineer were invited to visit Merck's factories in the United States, and at a meeting in Clonmel on 2 August 1972 the company presented its proposal for a plant to manufacture a range of bulk chemical products for export. The crucial incentive was the prospect of 450 jobs.

The response of the county council was favourable, and the following day Merck and Company applied for planning permission to build a chemical plant at Ballydine, ten miles east of Clonmel and four miles from Carrick-on-Suir. Two weeks later planning permission was granted, subject to compliance with recommendations set out in 1972 by the Institute for Industrial Research and Standards (IIRS)—now "Eolas"—which Merck had employed to help them carry out an assessment of the project. In March 1976 the company began manufacturing, employing 165 people.

On the rising ground just over a mile north-east of the factory the Hanrahans of Ballycurkeen sought advice about the plant from their friend and agricultural adviser, Dave Hurley. He approached the STDA and was assured there would be no problem. Accordingly the Hanrahans did not object to the planning permission, and in fact John Hanrahan helped to lay out the factory lawns.

The plant is neat and well manicured, but it remains nevertheless an intrusion on the Co Tipperary landscape. Occupying the space of a good-sized farm, it sits uneasily in the rural setting, its gleaming aluminium stacks dominating the skyline, puffing out great clouds of smoke and steam.

☐

One of the quiet revolutions of the last forty years has been the arrival of the organic chemical age, with carbon-based materials, mainly petroleum and natural gas, being converted into a huge variety of products, including the endless assortment of drugs we use to treat various diseases or indeed to help us cope with modern living.

What distinguishes the chemical industry is that its raw materials undergo fundamental change. In other industries materials are broken, bent, moulded or mixed together, but they retain their material integrity; in the chemical industry they are transformed into different substances. The new products can be as dangerous as the old ones or more so. There may also be products that are not needed, and disposing of these can lead to pollution; some of the better-known products and by-products are suspected of causing cancer and other serious illnesses.

Making organic chemicals is big business in the United States, which has more than a thousand plants producing them. Production there has increased tenfold since the Second World War; by comparison, production of all other chemicals over the same period has increased only fourfold, and all industrial production has merely doubled. In 1985 it was estimated that in the United States the organic chemical industry generates 60 per cent of the toxic waste entering the environment, whether buried in land-fills, released into water, or emitted into the air.

The small state of New Jersey, just across the Hudson River from New York City, is the organic chemical heartland of America. All the big companies have plants there: Du Pont, Ciba Geigy, Union Carbide, Allied Chemical, Squibb, Exxon, Scher Chemicals, and Merck and Company. From this tightly knit but competitive and often uncomfortable chemical nursery many companies have spread their wings and set up subsidiaries around the globe.

☐

In 1668 the Merck family began their chemical business in Germany. In 1887 they opened a branch in New York, and in 1903 they built a manufacturing plant in Rahway, New Jersey. In 1919 Merck became a wholly owned American company, and in 1953 it merged with another American company, Sharp and Dohme, to become Merck, Sharp and Dohme for manufacturing purposes. The parent is Merck and Company, with its head office in Rahway, New Jersey. Merck, Sharp and Dohme (Ireland) Ltd is registered in

Bermuda.

Over the years since 1933, when George W Merck established a research laboratory at Rahway, Merck scientists have been to the forefront in biomedical research. They played a part in developing penicillin, streptomycin, and cortisone, and pioneered research into drugs for the treatment of heart disease, arthritis, and depression. In the process they have made a lot of money. Merck is now the biggest pharmaceutical company in the world, employing over 37,000 people in a network of a hundred manufacturing plants, research laboratories, and experimental farms. Operations are scattered across the United States as well as in twenty-eight countries as far apart as Puerto Rico and Pakistan. About half Merck's sales come from activities outside the United States.

According to the journal *Merck Review,* Ireland was selected for several reasons. The company wanted access to EC markets, and Ireland had just voted to join. Ireland also had a plentiful supply of skilled labour, as well as tax incentives and grants for construction and employee training. The site at Ballydine had abundant water from the River Suir and was close to sea and air routes.

But environmentalists believe that Ireland was a haven for the chemical industry for other reasons. In an article in the *International Journal of Health Services* in 1979 Barry Castleman outlined the high cost of pollution control in the United States compared with other countries. As hazardous and polluting industries come under increasing regulation, some of the processes are exported to countries where cheap and uninformed labour is abundant. The produce is then sold to industrial countries, with the competitive advantage of not having to comply with costly pollution control regulations.

Enticing a company such as Merck to Co Tipperary was a big success for the STDA. But they were not content with just one factory in the area, and they continued their attempts to attract other companies. With the Merck plant under construction another American company, Schering

Plough, presented a proposal for an antibiotics plant. Again the county council was strongly in favour, but a local group organised opposition, on the grounds that the factory would be a dangerous source of pollution. The proposed site was nearer Clonmel, and at first the group had about two hundred objectors, many of them farmers. More in solidarity with their colleagues than in serious opposition, the Hanrahans lent their support to the lobby.

The debate was acrimonious. Eventually the group dwindled to only ten objectors, and they became the focus of a concerted campaign of intimidation. Cows were poisoned and released onto the road at night, broken glass was strewn on a driveway, a family was threatened by a mob, and others had to seek Garda protection. Children were shunned and threatened at school. Early one morning in December 1975 one of the opponents of the project found a coffin at his doorstep. The objectors were branded as cranks and publicity-seekers, and castigated by TDs, senators, and a Government minister.

At a public meeting in Cahir they were told from the platform that unless they withdrew their objections they would be ostracised. Eventually, in December 1975, the group felt obliged to issue a statement withdrawing their objections. "For the safety of our families and property we individually and collectively bow to the pressure of serious intimidation and threats of violence, which forces us to forgo our constitutional rights as citizens of this country. In these circumstances we individually and collectively withdraw our objections to the proposed industry and will take no further action."

It was a black day for democracy in Ireland, and all to no purpose: Schering Plough decided to set up elsewhere, because, they said, of the delays and objections. But in spite of their withdrawal the opposition lobby were not forgiven, and it was this bitter legacy that was inherited by the Hanrahan family of Ballycurkeen almost ten years later.

4

THE RED BOOK

27 December, 1980—Cow 50 had dead twins.
31 December, 1980—Cow 22 died frothing at the mouth.
6 January, 1981—Cow 283 had dead Friesian heifer calf.
8 January, 1981—Cow 260 had dead Friesian heifer.
10 January, 1981—Cow 277 died.
10 January, 1981—Cow 277's calf died.
22 January, 1981—Cow 263 had dead Friesian heifer calf.
29 January, 1981—Cow 288 had dead twins
31 January, 1981—Cow 288 died in severe pain.

On the morning of Wednesday 31 December 1980 John Hanrahan was up early to milk his cows as usual. In the shed he found a big Friesian cow lying dead with bubbles of froth at her mouth. The day before he had noticed the animal coughing and weeping, but in this she was no different from the rest of the herd at the time. Calf deaths no longer surprised him; but this was the first death of an adult animal. Four days previously another cow had given birth to dead twins.

These two incidents were the first entries in a death list that Selina Hanrahan began to record at the beginning of 1981; she later photocopied the list into what became known as the Red Book. It was a chronicle of life and death on the Ballycurkeen farm from 1981 to the middle of 1984, the basis of the Hanrahans' case against Merck. She recorded also what was happening to the family, and not least to herself.

In the early hours of Sunday 11 January Selina began to have a severe uterine haemorrhage. She woke her husband and he rushed her to Airmount Maternity Hospital in Waterford, twenty miles away. She spent a week in hospital, and on her return she resumed her record of events.

In the early days of 1981 the strain was beginning to tell on John Hanrahan. He was in the process of increasing the size of his dairy herd and had drafted in more young heifers than usual, and they were calving about this time. It would have been a difficult time anyway; but to compound the problem, John Hanrahan and his family were suffering similar symptoms themselves.

By the second week in February another disturbing development became evident. Hanrahan's 115-cow herd had produced six sets of twins, with over half of them yet to calve. Advised by Tom de Lacy, the Hanrahans began to feel that the matter needed wider official attention. De Lacy made contact with Pat Crowe, senior veterinary officer in charge of the Department of Agriculture's regional veterinary laboratory at Kilkenny, and sent him a stillborn calf for post-mortem examination, the first of many. No specific conclusion was reached on that occasion, and many of the later results from Kilkenny would be equally inconclusive.

Up to then Hanrahan had taken farm management advice mainly from Dave Hurley, retired chief agricultural officer and family friend. On 9 February, with Hurley, he approached the current chief agricultural officer, Michael English. They outlined the events at the farm and gave him a copy of the death list. English passed it on to the county council. A week later an official of the Department of Agriculture, Michael Hannifin, called to the farm and asked for the cattle identity cards. He produced a copy of Selina's death list, saying that his veterinary inspector thought a test should be done to find out if brucellosis was the cause of the deaths and deformities.

Brucellosis is a highly contagious disease that causes

cattle to abort prematurely. The Department of Agriculture had just begun to operate compulsory annual testing under the brucellosis eradication scheme. Animals that reacted positively, known as "reactors," had to be sent for slaughter; in addition, a restriction order was served until the herd had had two clear tests at sixty-day intervals. It meant that the farmer was forbidden to move cattle into or out of the herd except directly to an abattoir. To ensure that this order was adhered to, the department took possession of the animal identity cards. This often imposed great hardship on farmers, as compensation was felt to be inadequate and they were deprived of income from the sale of animals.

Faced with an official demand for identity cards, most farmers would have complied. But, showing the stubbornness that was to lead him eventually up the steps of the High Court, John Hanrahan refused. He pointed out that his cows had not aborted but carried a full nine months before producing a dead or deformed calf.

Hannifin told the court that Hanrahan's animals passed a brucellosis test two days later. He wrote out a restriction order and attached it to the herd file. It remained on the file but was never served or implemented. The animals never failed a compulsory brucellosis test, and Hanrahan continued to buy and sell. The family had built up a reputation in the locality for the quality of their breeding stock; any suggestion of brucellosis would damage that reputation and restrict their income in the long term, even without a restriction order.

It had been a crucial incident in developing Hanrahan's doubts about official good faith. He had brought the death list to the attention of the authorities in the hope of convincing them that his complaints were genuine, but he felt they had twisted the information and used it against him. No longer would he give information in confidence either to the county council or to the Department of Agriculture.

A few days later Hanrahan attached a tape recorder to his telephone and began to record his conversations. Over the next few years his conviction that people were not honouring commitments or standing by what they told him was frequently reinforced.

On 17 February 1981 Peter Dougan, a burly, quiet-spoken man in his mid-fifties, made the first of several visits to the Hanrahan farm at Ballycurkeen. He ran a veterinary practice from Clonmel and worked on a retainer basis for South Tipperary County Council. Of roughly a hundred cows in a shed he estimated that at least half were coughing and about the same number were "not thriving," the expression commonly used to describe an unhealthy appearance in animals. On Sunday 29 March Dougan went to the farm again, at John Hanrahan's request. The previous day Hanrahan had found his cattle red-eyed and weeping. Tom de Lacy had seen them early on Sunday and suggested that Dougan be called. The running eyes and noses were usually at their worst in the early morning; throughout the day the symptoms wore off but often reappeared overnight.

"I saw a shed full of cows," Dougan told the court, "and I would say 90 per cent of them had running eyes . . . There was three or four of them in a bad state and I took a swab. I took two swabs from each cow. I gave two to Mr Hanrahan and I sent two to Coolmore Stud [Laboratory] to see if they could find any cause of it bacterially or virally. I waited a fortnight to get the results from them and it came back negative."

The duplicate swabs were also tested at the Kilkenny laboratory and found to contain *Moraxella bovis*, a bacterial organism associated with infectious bovine keratitis (IBK), commonly known as "pink-eye." Although veterinary pathologists have yet to find the cause of pink-eye, this bacterium has been isolated in most swabs taken from affected animals; however, it has also been found in eyes showing no symptoms. "Lachrymation" or weeping is an early symptom of IBK, and if untreated this is followed by ulceration and a white or pinkish clouding over of the eyeball.

Crowe wrote to de Lacy informing him that *Moraxella*

had been found in the swabs but saying also that the clinical symptoms did not suggest this was the cause of the problem. He took samples from seven further animals a week later but found nothing.

On 25 March 1981 John and Selina Hanrahan were preparing grazing paddocks so they could release the cows kept indoors during the winter. They noticed that the grass appeared to be burnt, and got in touch with the agricultural adviser. A week later a team of scientists from An Foras Talúntais came to see it. They took samples and photographs, and as they walked the farm they noticed also that ivy on a row of trees facing the Merck factory was entirely burnt, while ivy on the opposite side of the trees was normal. No conclusive results emerged from the tests. Despite the burning, however, with winter silage all used up Hanrahan was forced to let the cows out on the grass.

During the following week the oppressive odours and fumes developed to a new level of intensity. At the same time Tommy Rockett was preparing to let his animals out on grass also. On 10 April 1981 he put 118 cattle into an eight-acre field of fresh pasture seeded the previous autumn, but they wouldn't eat the grass. "They didn't seem to like it, and when I went up a couple of evenings afterwards I put them into another field and they put down their heads and they sniffed the grass. They moved around it. That was unusual. When cattle go to fresh grass the Red Army wouldn't get them out. That was most unusual to me, and that behaviour continued."

Some days later the Hanrahans' cows began to kick the milking machine units off their udders. The udders and teats were found to be a reddish-purple colour and very sore. Peter Dougan was called again and he found that many of the cows had developed white blotches or lesions on the teats, and some of these had turned into little growths. Hanrahan gave him the history and said the animals had been seen by Tom de Lacy and his assistant and by Pat Crowe, who had taken samples for analysis at Kilkenny.

On 1 May Dougan's report was received by the county council. "Neither of the three veterinary surgeons had seen anything like it before. As quite apart from the teats the sides of some of the dugs [udders] were also affected, varying from side to side . . . Approximately 40 were affected the first day . . . On the 30 April 113 out of 131 cows were affected." In the meantime Pat Crowe produced a result of the test. Two of the five samples were positive for *Paravaccinia*, the virus that causes cow-pox.

Normally with cow-pox there are three phases: first there is what looks like a flea-bite, then a viscule or blister, and then a crust.

"When you were looking at these animals did they appear to have any of these three stages?" Tom Smyth, Hanrahan's counsel, asked Dougan.

"They just had the one."

"Did you think it was cow-pox?"

"No, because there was no sign of the other two."

"Could it have been mastitis?"

"No, it definitely wasn't mastitis. The milk wasn't affected."

"What was it?"

"I didn't know."

Hanrahan noticed that a group of dry cows left indoors to finish off a pit of silage was not affected by the ailment until he fed them a quantity of freshly cut grass. The animals lay on part of the grass left uneaten and soon developed sore udders also.

Tommy Rockett had animals grazing in two different fields within the same radius of the Merck factory, and the animals were refusing to eat in both places. As the weeks wore on he noticed that they got more and more unhappy and spent much of their time coughing, salivating, and attempting to throw up. Rockett believed their behaviour was due to irritation.

"Where was the irritation?" Dermot Gleeson, another of Hanrahan's barristers, asked him.

"Down the throat, down right to the stomach."

"What did that?"

"They started to cough; they get coughing."

"When would the coughing start?"

"The irritation developed into a cough, and the more grass they put into their mouths the more it would add to their irritation. In the finish it came in such a way they couldn't graze at all. It was all coughing. I was puzzled what to do. I knew it was on the pasture; the problem was the pasture."

Unlike the Hanrahans, before 1981 Rockett had had no indication of trouble from the Merck factory. "I had an open mind on the thing. I had an open mind."

"We are hearing about your open mind." Kevin Liston, Merck's counsel, was cross-examining. "I'm not sure what it means. Does an open mind mean that you suspected the factory must be the cause of the trouble?"

"I did."

"When did you start that suspicion?"

"All through May, June, July I had suspicions."

Rockett was a member of the local group that had lobbied for monitoring of air quality, but refused to believe the findings of Dr Jamieson's results indicating that acid concentrations in the air were well within safe limits. "A bullock is a monitor," Rockett, a direct and racy sixty-year-old, told the court. "He's one of the best monitors in the world. He'll sniff every bit of the grass he eats and if he doesn't like it he'll reject it . . . They wanted a clean grass, not polluted grass. That was definitely polluted. They know it, and I believe my animals."

He described how he had detected smells and fumes coming from the factory, some that could be seen and not smelt, some that were invisible but could be detected. "A range of different smells. You could get them out the fields. You could be walking out in the field and walking into the path of something and you could stop and it might be forty or fifty feet wide, and you could get another one and it would be so strong you wouldn't go through it. If you failed it would burn the eyes out of you."

Hanrahan's cows were showing a similar reluctance to eat. They began to vomit the grass along with a greenish fluid. Yet the grass looked normal enough, except for the burning in March and some burnt patches later. To compensate, Hanrahan continued to feed meals at the winter feeding rate.

It is standard practice to feed about fifteen pounds of concentrate meals a day to milking cows while they are feeding on silage indoors. But as soon as they are put to pasture in spring this is no longer economical. Grass is a complete diet. However, with Hanrahan's cows rejecting the grass, their milk yield was beginning to suffer, so he resorted to meal feeding to keep production up.

In the meantime Rockett's beef cattle were failing to thrive, and in June he began to sell them to the meat factory, long before they were ready for slaughter. Eventually he sold only 74 of his 118 cattle and held the remaining 44 until the following year, a most unusual deviation from his normal pattern.

Grass growth in Ireland is at its most luxurious between April and August, and during this period farmers harvest their surplus grass as hay and silage for winter feeding. Hanrahan began to have difficulty in harvesting his silage on 29 May 1981. The grass was an unusual dark colour, and the machine operator complained that instead of passing through the forage harvester normally it was tending to roll into lumps and wind itself around the auger. He also pointed out large pink patches on the ground where the grass had been cut.

After a few days in the pit the silage developed an unfamiliar repulsive smell, and the effluent that seeps out under the covering plastic as the grass ferments was a dirty yellow and black. When the effluent settled it grew a greasy film on top and later dried into a hard, creamy-white substance. A test done on a sample later by An Foras Talúntais failed to uncover any abnormality.

6 March, 1981—Cow 513 had deformed calf (died shortly afterwards)

10 March, 1981—A deformed calf was put down by vet
11 March, 1981—Cow 518 had dead fleck heifer
13 March, 1981—Cow 403 had small bull calf (Died shortly
afterwards)
5 April, 1981—Cow 284's five-weeks-old calf died
6 April, 1981—Fleck bull calf found dead in his house
11 April, 1981—Calf died
17 May, 1981—Friesian bull calf died
22 May, 1981—Friesian calf died
24 May, 1981—Three-weeks-old calf dropped dead
25 May, 1981—Cow 531's calf died

By the end of May Selina's death list ran to twenty-six animals. Seven of the smaller carcases had been sent to the Kilkenny laboratory, but no specific reasons for death could be found in five of them; the remaining two were reported as having died from meningitis and a condition described as "bawling calf syndrome." Tom de Lacy was not impressed by this diagnosis.

"What is the bawling calf syndrome?" Liston asked him.

"I think it's a bit of a farce."

"Would you tell us what it is?"

"Sometimes when you're feeding calves they drink very quickly and then they start to stagger and bawl and collapse and die. It's a well-known condition, but diagnosis would be problematic, and I think that's stated in the report."

One of the obstacles encountered according to Pat Crowe's reports was the advanced state of decomposition of some of the carcases that had been dead for some time before birth. There was nothing to indicate the cause of death—and nothing to bolster Hanrahan's confidence in the department.

☐

"We were milking the cows, my aunt and myself, and this dreadful odour came over with a dreadful burning effect. All the cows in the yard started to cough and their eyes were streaming. I rushed back into the milking parlour. I felt it burning my skin. I returned to the milking parlour, which I normally wouldn't do until I have a full row of cows. It takes ten cows on each side. I had roughly about eight in on the second side when I ran in, and by this stage my aunt was overcome. Both of us went into the house immediately and left the machine. It wasn't possible to take the machine off the cows. I phoned the factory."

It was 6.50 a.m. when Brian Doolan answered the telephone at the Merck security desk. John Hanrahan was excited. What were they doing? There was stuff coming over—it nearly choked his aunt—they had to stop the milking—he was overpowered. Would they stop it?

It was logged as complaint number 38 in Merck's odour complaints record. At 7.00 a.m. the production supervisor began his round of inspection. On the roof of the process building he found a very strong smell from the water cooling tower and a slight smell from the waste treatment area. His report also stated there was a hydrochloric acid release about an hour before the odour complaint, but this was not the cause of the odour.

Three products were being manufactured at the time, which between them use a wide variety of chemicals. The utilities supervisor, John Cunningham, also referred to the hydrochloric acid leak in his report on the same incident. "Process had a HCl leak on the west side of the building at 06.00 and fire crew were called out. Wind at time of complaint south-west." Cunningham checked the road on all sides of the Hanrahans' house and was unable to detect any odour. Yet the leak had needed the fire crew's attention. A light wind was blowing from the south-west, so emissions from Merck would have drifted slowly towards Ballycurkeen.

Later that morning John Hanrahan spoke on the phone to Merck's head of engineering, Frank Wyatt, who acknowledged that they had had a leak and that Hanrahan may have got a whiff of hydrochloric acid. "I apologise for the leak this morning and the smell of it. It probably was what you smelt, and I acknowledge that it did happen."

They went on to debate the nature of the smell and the time it had happened. "I don't know what time the leak actually happened," Wyatt continued; "in fact I don't think anybody knows, because—"

"Well, I'll tell you. I could give you definite times on it if I was at the house, because I know my family were up during the night over it, and I know I woke up and I couldn't open my bloody eyes this morning."

But it is possible that what the Hanrahans detected that morning was not just the hydrochloric acid from the spillage. Hydrochloric acid was one of the products emitted from the waste incinerator, which was in use on 11 June but is not mentioned in the company's reports on the complaint.

Six complaints were recorded by Merck in June 1981, two from the Hanrahans and four from Perigoe's pub, both in the same north-east line from the factory. Dr Jamieson's monitors were in place since April 1981 measuring acid and organics in the air. The highest acid levels measured during the year-long test were recorded in June 1981, but they were well within safe limits and below the levels that could be detected by smell or cause irritation. This contradiction was to remain at the heart of the Ballydine conflict.

Merck staff were increasingly sceptical of Hanrahan's complaints, and indeed those of others. They were getting on average one complaint a week, and the routine was to check the factory premises and perimeter and the area the complaint was reported from. But regularly they reported finding only "farmyard smells" at the site of the complaint. According to the general manager, Declan Buckley, their own personnel were able to confirm complaints in only 30 per cent of cases.

□

At milking time on 12 July 1981 cow 130 began to tremble and show signs of agitation. Thinking it was an attack of milk fever, Hanrahan released the cow from the milking machine and went to call the vet. When he got back the cow had collapsed in the yard. He went to call the vet again and on his return found the cow on her feet, walking about but apparently in great pain.

Milk fever affects milking cows at the height of their lactation, as a result of loss of body calcium with the milk. The level is gradually depleted unnoticed until it reaches a critical point, when the cow suddenly begins to tremble and usually collapses. Treatment is an immediate injection of calcium, and rarely will an animal get up again without it. Most farmers recognise the condition and call the vet or give the injection themselves. Tom de Lacy arrived and began the milk fever treatment, but the cow collapsed again and died, writhing in pain, with bubbles oozing from her eyes and mouth. Hanrahan remembered finding a dead cow six months previously with bubbles at her mouth also. De Lacy was unable to make a diagnosis on this occasion either.

Two days earlier a weanling heifer had died, and the following morning they found another weanling dead. De Lacy decided to send all three animals to the Kilkenny laboratory. Some days later Pat Crowe sent the results, showing that one of the calves and the cow had evidence of internal bleeding, suggesting blood poisoning or contact with something toxic such as rat poison or bracken. There was no rat poison on the farm, and no bracken. The third animal had extensive duodenal ulceration with perforation and peritonitis. Crowe's report said ulceration had been associated with mouldy hay. The other calf was badly decomposed, but its intestines were "extremely hyperaemic and had blood-stained contents."

For 12 August 1981 the Red Book records that Tom de Lacy came to attend to two heifers that had begun to pass blood in the urine. They did not respond to de Lacy's treatment for "red-water," a bacterial infection of the blood transmitted by ticks picked up on old pasture. Neither were the red-water bacteria found in a blood sample sent for analysis to Kilkenny. These were the first of many examples of such bleeding, often accompanied by bleeding from the eyes, nose, and bowel.

In September 1981 Selina Hanrahan went to the Infirmary Hospital in Waterford with a bleeding ulcer. She needed a blood transfusion, and spent two weeks in hospital. She was given the usual treatment for a stomach ulcer, but the Hanrahan family and their advisers saw it as yet another example of a condition common to humans and animals.

□

Throughout July and August the animals' condition deteriorated. They had running eyes and noses repeatedly and began to cough and show respiratory distress with increasing frequency. They were refusing to eat the grass and "vomiting the cud," and meal feeding had to be continued, along with large amounts of bread soda. The second cut of silage was no better than the first, and with winter approaching Hanrahan was worried about its condition and safety. On 28 August Pat Crowe was called again from Kilkenny.

"On this occasion," Crowe reported, "I noticed many of the cows were showing respiratory distress and coughing and had lost condition. The weanlings showed a high incidence of coughing. I suggested also that silage be sampled and examined by Mr Hanrahan's adviser."

A month later de Lacy asked Peter Dougan to call again to examine a large number of animals with respiratory distress. He examined forty-one cows, two bullocks and one bull and reported all as having pulmonary complaints. Dougan said later he did not believe the widespread respiratory distress was the condition known as hoose, caused by lungworms, nor was it virus pneumonia, which occurs in winter when animals are indoors. He sent his second report to the county council describing what he had found, drawing attention also to the Kilkenny post-mortem result of internal bleeding in a cow and to Selina's internal bleeding.

Tests on two calf carcases at Kilkenny in September showed no evidence of lungworm or other parasites, although one of the animals did have pneumonia. But at the end of October five out of six sets of weanling lungs examined had evidence of hoose. The sixth had enzootic pneumonia, caused by viral or bacterial infection.

"How did this complaint arise?" Tom Smyth asked de Lacy.

"By the intake of worm eggs, which develop into a worm in the throat of the animal, in the trachea. In small doses it causes pneumonia, or very often death. But our treatment has been quite satisfactory all along, but in this year, in 1981, the animals were treated the same. They were dosed regularly for worms . . . and then they were housed, and it must have been a month after their being housed they developed this hoose pneumonia, which is very unusual once you dose them and put them in. They don't get reinfected. These didn't respond to treatment to it and I think there were six lost that year that showed hoose pneumonia."

"Why do you think that occurred? Were you able to ascertain why that occurred?"

"No. What appeared to have happened in the herd that year is that their resistance seemed to be lowered to all types of infection."

None of the five vets who visited the farm at the time diagnosed hoose as the cause of the widespread breathing difficulty. Hoose is a disease so obvious that most farmers can readily identify it. It would hardly have escaped the notice of five vets.

☐

In early October meetings were called at Hanrahan's and Rockett's to discuss the animal health situation in the locality. Attending with local farmers and residents were senior members of the IFA and ICMSA, the two main farming organisations. The group decided to ask the county council for the up-to-date results of the air quality monitoring. Eventually a progress report was made available, but it shed little further light on the problem.

At this time the health of the Hanrahan herd had reached a low ebb. They were intermittently coughing, choking, discharging from the eyes and nose, losing condition, and vomiting. As grass growth had diminished so also had the sore udders, but other problems continued to arise. Twelve sets of twins had been born in twelve weeks, and the animals' hormone balance appeared to be disturbed. They had hair loss, scruffy skin, and overgrown hooves, and were generally drowsy and sluggish.

Tom de Lacy brought the situation to the attention of the Veterinary Faculty at UCD and picked out three cows typical of a group showing the worst respiratory distress. In the first week of October the three animals were delivered to the veterinary college for observation, tests, and eventually post-mortem examination. Two of the cows were diagnosed as having diffuse fibrosing alveolitis, a lung condition whose cause is unknown; the report said one of them may have developed the condition from badly saved hay. The diagnosis for the third cow was broncho-pneumonia, caused by commonly occurring bacteria. Three years later in the High Court these results would be the subject of sharp debate.

□

The night of 20 October 1981 was clear, moonlit and calm in Ballycurkeen. At about 1.00 a.m. Tommy Rockett was getting ready for bed when his wife called him to see a huge cloud rising from the Merck factory, clearly visible in the floodlights. They drove down to the factory and counted seven vents on the roof belching emissions into a huge stationary cloud sitting a hundred feet above the complex. There was no smell.

"I had a handkerchief over my mouth," Rockett said,

"and my nose dried up with inhaling, and I had to breathe through my mouth. My lips got wooden." Realising their farm was in the fall-out range of the emissions, he said he and his wife had been very frightened. They had driven home quickly, but they made no complaint either to the factory or the county council.

At 10.30 p.m. on Wednesday 4 November John Hanrahan and Tommy Rockett drove into Rockett's farmyard. The light wind was south-west, and a thin veil of fog hung over the Suir valley. The two men had been to an IFA meeting discussing their animal health situation. On opening the car doors they were confronted by a "dreadful smell of chemicals." They drove to Ballydine and into a laneway running along the factory boundary.

"As we were driving up towards the factory," Rockett recalled, "we could see an emission coming off from some of the flues or chimney stacks, but some of it came in through the window of the car, and we drove back and we said—"

"Don't say what was said," Gleeson interrupted the flow. "What did you experience? What did you feel?"

"I felt when I smelt it I knew immediately what it was, and I saw the wind direction: 'twas flowing up towards my land and I knew that 'twould be coming down on the pasture, and I said, 'More sore mouths next week, and we're in an awful mess here . . . We have to do something about it . . .' I said I was going to ring the county manager while that emission was going on and ask him to come down and tell him about it and explain the animal problems."

Eventually, after midnight, Hanrahan managed to speak to the county manager, Tom Rice, at his home. Shortly afterwards he had a call from Merck to say they were investigating. At about 2.30 a.m. Rice arrived with two other officials, but by then the smell had disappeared. They were given a long explanation of the problems by Hanrahan, his mother, and Rockett; but the late hour and the circumstances of the complaint did not improve relations.

☐

Pat Crowe visited the farm again on 24 November and took vaginal swabs from the cows, and examined a number of cows in detail. "All age groups were showing increased respiration and coughing," he reported. "Level of thrift in stock is low, and compares unfavourably with the general condition of the herd when I first inspected it on February 11, 1981." He made no mention of hoose at that time.

No pathogens were found in the swabs but Crowe did arrive at conclusions from 111 blood samples examined between 22 September and 3 November at Kilkenny. He found low copper levels, anaemia, and evidence of lungworm attack, but no pathogens that would account for running noses and weeping. These results would be the subject of further sharp disagreement in the High Court.

By this time Tom Rice had begun to feel that the issue extended beyond the county council's sphere of competence, and on 10 December 1981 he invited representatives of relevant state bodies to a meeting in Clonmel. It was attended by Pat Crowe and Michael Hayes (Department of Agriculture), Dr Ian Jamieson and Bill MacCluskey (An Foras Forbartha), two scientists from An Foras Talúntais, Michael English (chief agricultural officer), Dr de Souza (county medical officer), Jim O'Callaghan (county engineer), Peter Dougan, and a number of other county council officials.

Rice outlined the problems, with particular attention to Hanrahan's complaints, and Jamieson reported on his measurements of air quality, showing that it was meeting accepted standards. Crowe described the deteriorating condition of Hanrahan's herd, and English explained that Hanrahan was a highly organised and efficient farmer. It was suggested that the Department of Agriculture might do further investigations, and Rice said these should centre on the Merck factory itself. The report of the meeting gives no indication that only the previous month the company had admitted to the county council in writing that emissions from its plant had exceeded their planning permission severalfold.

☐

"What happened the rabbits?" Tom Smyth was getting Mary Hanrahan to elaborate on the fate of the children's pets.

"I had a lot, you know, surplus vegetables in the garden, and the rabbits were fed from the vegetables taken to the kitchen, the outer leaves of cabbages and lettuces and all these things. I think there was three rabbits the younger boy had at the time."

"Ambrose."

"Yes. He was feeding those rabbits on that kind of food, and one rabbit died. We didn't take much notice of it, because these things happen. After a time the rabbits became sick again, and all the animals were very sick at this time, all the animals were passing red water."

Tom de Lacy was treating the cattle when he noticed the rabbits passing blood also. He advised them to stop feeding vegetables and greens from the garden.

"Anyway, they were fed on meals then, and Ambrose was very sorry for the rabbits, and he again, some time later he went back and fed them the vegetables, and shortly after that a rabbit died."

They sent it to the Department of Agriculture's Veterinary Research Laboratory at Abbotstown, Co Dublin, and at the same time they sent a sample of fresh vegetables for analysis to the Public Analyst's Laboratory in Cork. Both the rabbit and the outer leaves of the vegetables were found to have high levels of cadmium and lead. The normally timid rabbits developed aggressive and vicious behaviour, and all died. By then the family stopped using the vegetables, because throughout 1981 Mary had noticed other strange developments in the garden. Cabbages grew to be about four-and-a-half feet tall; delphiniums grew seven feet tall; leeks, beans, Jerusalem artichokes, runner bean roots grew to enormous sizes. Tomato plants failed to produce fruit; nettle leaves were burnt; ivy withered on trees; and snowberry leaves developed white deposits. At the end of the year she gave up gardening

By the end of 1981 Mary Hanrahan's sister Wilhemena

was suffering respiratory congestion and generally poor health, and Charles and Ambrose did not escape either: they suffered headaches, nausea, nosebleeds, running eyes and noses, and sore throats. In November John and Selina were called to the school when the children were found crying and rubbing their eyes, although none of the other pupils were affected. "Their eyes were streaming," Selina explained, "and all the white of their eyes had burned red . . . They were examined by the doctor and he told us they were affected by some sort of irritant."

During 1981 all the family had made several visits to the doctor, and Selina had been to hospital twice with internal bleeding. The children also spent time in hospital. Compounding their distress was the mental cost of grappling with the unknown, and the mounting financial burden. A vet had called to the farm almost every day, and the symptoms of animal distress, first noted seriously a year before, were epidemic by now.

By the year's end Selina had made forty-six entries in the death list.

5

NEIGHBOURS

Approaching the shed, Ger Clancy heard the coughing and an eerie sort of moan he would have said was the wind, except that there was none that day. Inside were about twenty cows. What struck him most was their thin, wasted appearance. Some were standing, chewing the cud, some were barely able to stand, and some were lying out flat. Many were moaning and wheezing in obvious distress. He noticed darkish encrusted matter at the corners of their eyes and extending down their faces.

It was his first visit to Hanrahan's farm, three days after Christmas 1981, and his second day at work with Tom de Lacy's veterinary practice.

He put his stethoscope to one cow's chest and listened. Through the regular thumping heartbeat he detected a reedy hiss with the intakes of breath. It sounded like bronchitis. With the stethoscope on another cow he picked up an advanced example of the reedy hiss he had detected in the first cow, but louder, more strident, more widespread. There was little he could do; and three days later the cow was dead.

What appeared to be premature labour was one of the strangest phenomena displayed by Hanrahan's herd. Another was the appearance of mating behaviour in pregnant animals, what farmers call "bulling" or "heat." Yet another development was lack of libido in a number of bulls, what Tom Smyth referred to as "bulls rejecting their calling."

Post-mortem results from the Kilkenny laboratory left ample room for different interpretations of the origin of the fatal condition. Of the twenty-eight autopsies done there during 1981 and 1982, lung damage was listed as the cause of death in thirteen cases. Six of that thirteen had evidence of lungworm, and four had evidence of enzootic pneumonia.

So the two commonly occurring diseases of young cattle, hoose and enzootic pneumonia, between them accounted for ten deaths in those two years—five deaths a year. It would not be an abnormal incidence in a herd of Hanrahan's size. The remaining three lung cases were adult cows that showed evidence of pulmonary oedema. One calf had meningitis, and there was no specific finding in the remaining fourteen autopsies.

Hanrahan's scepticism about the results from Kilkenny was increasing. In early March 1982 he drove to the laboratory with one of his advisers and asked to see the slides on which the results were based. Crowe told him the slides had not been retained.

☐

Selina continued to have treatment for the duodenal ulcer she had developed in September 1981, and was still following a strict diet in early February 1982 when uterine bleeding started again. This time she was rushed to the Aut Even Hospital in Kilkenny. She was there for two weeks, but was no sooner home than she was back again in March with another haemorrhage. On her discharge she went to stay with her sister in England.

John found a rented house in Piltown, ten miles away, and when Selina returned in early April they moved there with the two boys. There was an immediate improvement. For the first time in four years they could be sure of waking in the morning without running eyes. The worst of the headaches and nausea disappeared, and the family shook off the lethargy that afflicted them. John drove to Bally-curkeen each morning and would sometimes drive over at night also to attend to cows calving. But Mary refused to budge. She and Wilhemena remained behind in Bally-curkeen.

□

Liam Ryan is a tall, dark, strong-boned man in his late forties. He works as production clerk at the Merck factory and was also shop steward for the ITGWU. He cycled the two-and-a-half miles to work every day from his home in Kilsheelan, due west of Ballydine. "There was no worker ever left Ballydine due to a sick problem," he told the court. "There is nothing there abnormal."

"In terms of the physical environment—I want to ask you where you worked before you went to Ballydine," Nicholas Butler, one of the Merck legal team, asked.

"I worked at the garage business for nineteen or twenty years."

"Had you any other experience?"

"I worked in heavy industry in Manchester and the north of England."

"How did the working environment compare with there?"

"It wouldn't compare at all with Ballydine. Ballydine is a top-class establishment. I'm not saying that because I'm working there."

"Have you or any of your family at home in the village experienced any problem from the plant?"

"The only smell we get there is a smell from a local piggery. We get that in the summer-time. We don't get any smells from Ballydine."

A serious obstacle to Hanrahan's efforts at convincing Merck of their problems was the experience of the 250 people working at the Ballydine plant. They were handling dangerous materials every day. If they were showing no symptoms of trouble and making no complaints, why should they believe that the Hanrahans were anything but cranks?

Dr Michael Carey is a general practitioner in Clonmel, a former president of the Society of Occupational Medicine and a member of the American Occupational Medical Association. He is paid to provide a medical service to the Ballydine workers. He had acted in that capacity since 1974, when the plant was being built, co-ordinating the medical aspects of recruitment. "The basis on which I work," he told the court, "is that no individual should be damaged by his work situation throughout his working life, and we look at people and we try to make sure that they are not damaged by the working situation."

Employees are subject to comprehensive medical surveillance, depending on the work they do. Those in the production area have blood tests every six months and a full examination once a year; the remainder have a full examination every second year. If health problems arise they are dealt with by the full-time nurse on the premises or by Dr Carey, who attends three days a week. Absenteeism is less than 3 per cent, compared with a national average of about 10 per cent.

"Have you come across any people in the factory who are complaining of chest pains?" Kevin Liston was taking Carey through the health tests.

"Not really. We may occasionally get somebody with a chest cold but it is rare. I have not seen anybody complain of wheezing or tightness of the chest like that, definitely not." Skin rashes and dermatitis were the only work-related complaint, with seven or eight cases a year. They generally arose from accidental direct contact with the materials being used in the plant. One man lost his job because of recurring dermatitis. There were a few cases of eye irritation, but the staff at the plant are very well protected. Anyone who goes inside must wear goggles and safety glasses, and they are equipped with masks and breathing apparatus to be used if needed. Inside the process building the ventilation system achieves up to twelve complete air changes an hour. Any fumes or gases are quickly exhausted through the air vents in the roof.

There was a routine test for low white blood cell count, such as might result from exposure to chemical solvents, but there had never been a low count since the test began in 1978, when benzene was used in the plant. Only one abnormal blood test arose, unrelated to the work.

The factory routine made provision for complaints from the staff, and a number were logged from that source, but most complaints were coming from outside, suggesting that the odour, fumes and gases from emissions were being blown away from the plant.

The record shows that from May 1979 to the end of 1981 there were 150 complaints, mainly from the plant's nearest neighbours and usually when sulindac was being manufactured. The Hanrahans were only third in the league, making seventeen complaints by the end of 1981.

Noel Perigoe, whose pub is 500 yards from the main process building in the same north-easterly direction, made eighty-three complaints in that period. Typically the smells were described as lasting five to ten minutes, but sometimes for a whole day and once for a whole week. Two complaints were made when the plant was shut for the holiday period. On only eight of the eighty-three occasions did Merck personnel report finding an odour at the pub when they investigated.

Ray Foley, whose farm is directly east of the factory, made twenty-five recorded complaints by the end of 1981. The smells were described as lasting from ten minutes to three weeks. Again, most of the time the Merck staff reported finding no odour at the farm.

The pattern was the same at the Hackett farm, half a mile east of the factory: seventeen complaints were made in the period. Complaints came from a dozen other residents within a two-mile radius of the plant.

While Merck readily admitted that their emissions were the source of odour complaints from time to time, they were emphatic that such emissions, though mildly distressing, were no danger to animal or human health. The company's argument was that whatever health problems there may have been on the Hanrahan farm were unique to the farm and the result of internal rather than external factors. They were at pains to point out that none of the other farms in the neighbourhood were having problems.

Among the group of Ballydine residents formed at the end of 1980 to express concern about the factory were at least a dozen farmers. It included John and Mary Hanrahan, Tommy Rockett, Noel Perigoe, and Dick Tobin, a member of the county council. They had finally prevailed on the council to set up Dr Jamieson's second air quality study, and continued to meet after that. At the end of October 1981 a delegation met the Minister for the Environment, Peter Barry. They impressed on him that they did not want the factory closed but rather controlled. On 10 November 1981 an official from the department visited the factory and farms in the area accompanied by the county engineer, Jim O'Callaghan. There was no public outcome, though the results were to emerge a year later.

Early in 1982 John Hanrahan made contact through his brother-in-law with Dr Rory Finegan, a Canadian biologist and environmental consultant. In March 1982 Finegan arrived at Ballycurkeen and began an inspection of plant and animal life on the Hanrahan farm and other farms in the area. His arrival coincided with a period of intense public interest in the activities of Merck at Ballydine.

On 3 May 1982 Finegan addressed a meeting in Carrick-on-Suir chaired by John Kinsella, an engineer from Carlow. The meeting was attended by farmers and farm workers, factory workers, publicans, public representatives, members of the Alliance for Safety and Health, and Dr de Souza. Finegan had looked at the preliminary results of Dr Jamieson's monitoring, which had completed a twelve-month cycle in April. He told the meeting that Jamieson had reported the presence of an organic compound called monochlorobenzene in the air. Finegan explained that this was like a fingerprint, as it does not occur naturally and could only have come from the factory. The local topography was conducive to trapping emissions in the valley, and he mentioned the possibility of dioxins and other toxic and dangerous products.

Tom de Lacy listed the animal health problems on the Hanrahan farm, which, he said, reached an abnormal level in 1981. He had been hesitant about Merck's culpability at first but was now convinced the problem was the factory.

Hanrahan, Rockett and some others described how their cattle were coughing and refusing to eat grass. Michael English said that analysis of soil, grass and silage were all normal, and unless you know what to look for the analysis could go on indefinitely.

A number of residents raised the health problems they and their families were having: sickness, headaches, blocked noses, rashes, and respiratory difficulties. Dr de Souza said there were complaints of respiratory difficulties, burning sensation and watery eyes, but though it was reasonable to assume that they were caused by the chemical plant, there was no conclusive proof.

A further meeting on 15 June was chaired by Dave Hurley, the retired chief agricultural officer and former member of the development association. He said the factory was a great asset to the area but it should not interfere with people's life-styles or the environment. The meeting was attended by a number of farmers and other residents who complained of illness, coughing and respiratory problems as before and sought answers from the experts. The IFA representatives spoke of their futile attempts to have the monitoring continued at all sides of the factory. Attempts were made to form a committee, and eventually the meeting decided to send a delegation to meet the county manager.

This delegation met Tom Rice and the county council on 6 July 1982, but John Hanrahan was excluded, on the grounds that he had begun legal proceedings against Merck. It appeared that the council had aligned itself with the company. Rice said that Dr Jamieson's report was not yet ready but that it was unlikely to show that Merck was the cause of the problems. No reports from Hanrahan's experts had come to the council, and Rice wondered if the delegation could throw some light on that. At the suggestion that only the Hanrahans had problems Tom de Lacy pointed out that many others were complaining. He questioned the good faith of the county council, and left the meeting himself. In the meantime Dr Jameson, alarmed at developments in the area, had enlisted the aid of the Botany Department at TCD to undertake a biological study.

☐

The Suir valley is an area of large and fertile farms given to mixed enterprises. The commonest is "drystock and tillage," the system used by Hanrahan's nearest neighbour, Tommy Rockett. With this system about half the farm is cultivated with a cash crop like grain or sugarbeet and the remainder used for grazing beef cattle and sometimes sheep. Cattle are bought in the spring or autumn and held for not more than a year before being sold for slaughter. By and large there are no breeding stock and no young stock on such farms.

Of Hanrahan's immediate neighbours only Pat Walsh is a dairy farmer. His 200-acre farm adjoins Hanrahan's on the opposite side from the factory in the path of the prevailing south-west wind. While most of Hanrahan's land is sloping gently down towards Ballydine, Walsh's land slopes very gently away from the factory. In 1981 Walsh ran a 100-cow dairy herd and raised all the progeny for beef, apart from heifers reared as replacements for the dairy herd. It was essentially the same system as Hanrahan's except that he had more beef animals and somewhat fewer dairy animals. In March and April 1981 Walsh lost more than twenty calves out of approximately a hundred, an exceptionally high mortality rate. According to his brother Brendan Walsh, who was also his vet, the deaths were due to an *Escherichia coli* infection, which causes diarrhoea or white scour in calves; this opinion was based on the results of a laboratory test from Kilkenny. Walsh said that another farmer in Piltown, about ten miles away, had a similar problem that year. Pat Walsh's cattle also suffered from running eyes, which his brother attributed to pink-eye.

"Have you had experience there with cattle with running eyes as distinct from pink-eye?" Kevin Liston asked him, referring to the Ballydine area.

"Not that I am aware of. Any running eyes I meet I have probably treated them as pink-eye. You cannot be dogmatic. You have pink-eye, and if you get a call to animals with sore eyes you see them with tears down their faces and you have a look, and sometimes you can see the cornea is opaque and sometimes you can't. It's just tears. I normally inject all those. I couldn't tell you it is pink-eye with my hand on my heart."

Quite a few of the animals in the same location were passing blood in the urine. Martin Fitzgerald, Brendan Walsh's partner, diagnosed red-water and vaccinated the whole group for that, and one animal got two blood transfusions. Nevertheless a number of the animals died. So in 1981 the dairy farm adjoining Hanrahan's had deaths of a similar magnitude relatively, and animals suffering from running eyes and blood in the urine. But the respective veterinary practices, de Lacy's and Walsh's, came to different conclusions about the cause of these problems.

John Callanan has a 112-acre dairy farm on the southern side within the same radius of the factory. He was worried about his family inhaling emissions, and made a number of complaints. He seldom had an animal death, even in young animals, he said, but the mortality rate began to rise in the early eighties. A heifer took ill with what he thought was red-water, but he found no evidence of blood in the urine. A cow died just after calving for no apparent reason, and another developed what the vet, Brendan Walsh, thought was salmonella poisoning, but a post-mortem examination at Kilkenny showed no evidence of *salmonella* pathogens. A cow that swelled up before death was found to have widespread cancer, and yet another died of internal bleeding.

Four miles due west of Ballydine John Widger lost over forty animals in 1981. Five of his seventy-five milking cows died, and nine others had wasted to the point where he felt it more prudent to send them to the factory than have them die on the farm. Thirteen calves died at birth or were born dead, and three more died soon after birth. Thirteen weanlings died. Late the previous year almost the whole herd had developed running eyes, and many appeared to be sick. At the same time Widger noticed dead ivy on trees on the side facing the factory, and burnt patches of grass in the fields.

Two other dairy farmers, Ned Hearne and John Tobin, reported running eyes and noses, sore teats, overgrown hooves, twinning and hoose in their animals, but they did not blame the factory for these.

John Wallace's farm is on high ground about six miles to the north-east of the factory, and he also rented land two-and-a-half miles from the factory in the same direction. In September 1982 a group of thirty animals on the home farm developed running eyes and noses. Three of them became very ill, with high temperatures and breathing distress. On another occasion a group of a hundred animals on the farm nearer the factory began to stampede for no apparent reason, a phenomenon also reported by Hanrahan and others. Wallace blamed the stampeding and the illness on Merck emissions.

Tom Kiely had a drystock herd on his farm to the east of Hanrahan's and was also a butcher, supplying meat to the factory canteen. His evidence was that he had no animal health problems that he would attribute to the factory emissions. However, he had been in the dairy business until 1981 and suffered a number of calf deaths in a very short period during that year. Soon after that he sold out his dairy herd.

Just across the river, Martin Long detected smells from the factory, but his vet attributed severe coughing in his beef cattle to lungworm. Likewise, the death of thirty pregnant eses was blamed on poor diet rather than factory emissions.

Less than a mile west of the factory gates John Kehoe's 200-acre farm straddles the Clonmel–Waterford road. Kehoe himself was a member of South Tipperary County Council, and his son worked in the Merck factory. Kehoe said he had never had any problems with his animals since Merck began operations. He had a mixture of farm enterprises— tillage, sheep, and beef cattle. In the middle of 1983 he sold a group of thirteen cattle to a farmer near Carrick-on-Suir, about four miles away. Before the sale some of the animals were dehorned; this is a reasonably simple operation for a vet, but in this case one of the animals did not heal properly and continued to bleed intermittently. Several weeks later Ger Clancy was called, and he noticed also that the animals were subdued and lethargic. Apart from the dehorning wound, one animal was bleeding from the bowel and another from the nose. Accustomed to bleeding in Hanrahan's cattle, Clancy decided to have blood and bone marrow samples taken for testing at Kilkenny. All the blood samples showed low white cell counts and a moderate degree of aplastic anaemia, a condition that interferes with the blood clotting mechanism. The Kilkenny report also said that "the bone marrow smears showed evidence of toxic effect." Suspecting bracken poisoning, Clancy's partner, Tom de Lacy, inspected Kehoe's farm, where the cattle had come from, but found no bracken.

Just before the High Court case began in February 1985 a thirteen-page letter of complaint arrived at the Merck factory from a local farmer, Davy Cahill. He lived on a small beef farm just over two miles north of the factory and had never complained before. Like his neighbour John Kehoe, he kept about thirty breeding beef cows on his farm and had noticed no health problem. But in May 1984 he suddenly lost eleven three-month-old calves out of a total of seventy animals. His vet, Brendan Walsh, diagnosed the trouble as virus pneumonia, and treated them with penicillin. But Cahill suspected the factory emissions as the source of the problem, as he had previously known virus pneumonia as a disease that struck animals indoors in winter, not in May on grass. He pointed out that all his five children were in third-level education and he wanted to see them employed in Ireland, so he had a vested interest in having industries like Merck in the country. Nevertheless he did not want employment at any price, and felt the Suir valley was paying too highly.

Directly across the river from the Merck factory Paddy O'Meara had a drystock farm with cattle and sheep. In 1983 he told the news magazine *Magill* of an occasion in May 1981 when his cattle and sheep began to sniff the air and stampede as a thick fog descended on the field where they were grazing. He could feel a burning in his chest, and later felt weak and sore. In the middle of that night he woke unable to draw breath, and the following day the doctor could only suggest that he may have been in contact with poison. O'Meara began to lose weight and was sick for several months. The cattle in the field that day in May had faded away, and he sold them to a dealer for half their value. All but two of the twenty-four ewes there at the same time were found to be barren the following year, and he sold them as such.

☐

On 18 January 1982 Tom de Lacy wrote to Merck, to the county manager and the county medical officer, asking them "what chemical processes are carried out at the MSD plant at Ballydine and what substances waste or otherwise are released into the atmosphere."

Rice replied on 1 February, saying, "The information requested in your letter can best be obtained from Merck, Sharp and Dohme." On 24 February he received a reply from Dr de Souza. "The management of Merck, Sharp and Dohme have informed me that I am not at liberty to disclose confidential information which they have supplied me."

On the same day he got his reply from Byron Roe, the then general manager of Merck, saying, "The chemical processes are confidential and could not be revealed to an individual."

☐

On 22 February 1982 the Hanrahans put themselves outside the category of crank by issuing legal proceedings against Merck, Sharp and Dohme. They sought an order "restraining the Defendants from discharging noxious, toxic or deleterious smells, substances or fumes over and on to a farm belonging to the Plaintiffs," and claimed damages arising out of the same discharge. In so doing they reinforced the hostility that was slowly but surely developing between the family and Merck and indeed between the family and the county council.

From then on two conflicting images typified the gulf between the protagonists: on one side John Hanrahan, highly strung, persistent, convinced the factory activities were at the root of his family's problems; opposing him a multinational chemical company, preoccupied with its own manufacturing processes, impatient with complaints it saw as unduly fastidious.

That gulf became steadily wider.

6

PUBLIC PRESSURE

On 19 April 1982 the Hanarahans' solicitors lodged a statement of claim in the High Court. It accused Merck of causing toxic, corrosive, noxious and dangerous vapours, fumes, gases, dusts, liquids and other substances to be discharged from the company's lands at Ballydine, causing death and injury to the Hanrahans' stock and damage to buildings, equipment, crops, and pasture. It sought an order restraining the company from allowing such discharges from the plant, and sought damages for nuisance, trespass, negligence, and breach of duty.

Hanrahan had also become the focal point for widespread concern in the area about the plant emissions. Merck were aware that the meetings in May and June were attended by a cross-section of residents, and they knew that disturbing remarks had been made about the nature of their business. "In 1982 a number of meetings had been held in the area," Declan Buckley, Merck's general manager, told the court, "at which allegations were made about our operation and disparaging comments made about it by certain individuals. Resulting from that there was a good deal of concern generated, and we decided we had better allay that concern and we invited our neighbours, near neighbours, except Mr Hanrahan, to the plant in June of 1982."

About sixty people took up the invitation to visit the factory on 24 June. The general manager, Byron Roe, outlined the commercial importance of the company to the community and the country. He gave a brief description of the products and the manufacturing processes, explaining that many of the raw materials used were corrosive and hazardous unless handled with care. He explained the company's policy on safety and health: "Merck is committed to a policy of compliance with the spirit and letter of applicable laws and regulations concerning waste water discharge, air pollution emissions, solids disposal, and noise abatement."

He went on to explain that £2.2 million had been spent on a waste water treatment system and £270,000 to minimise odours. The odours were associated with thioanisole, which, he said, was non-toxic but could be smelt at very low concentrations. It was important to remember that controlled discharges to rivers or the atmosphere are not harmful or polluting. "As long as the levels discharged are within the capability of the environment to assimilate them, no damage is done."

Planning permission levels were established with large safety factors. There was testing where necessary to monitor what was being emitted; and analysis of the atmosphere in the area by Dr Jamieson had shown their emissions to be safe. In particular, Roe said, plant employees who received safe but greater exposure than anyone outside the plant did not experience unusual problems.

In conclusion he emphasised Merck's intention to be a good neighbour, and as proof of this he gave a list of donations the company had made to support education, health and civic projects, both locally and nationally. Since 1976 the value of these donations had amounted to over £250,000, and in 1982 about £70,000 would be distributed. The beneficiaries included most of the local primary and secondary schools from Clonmel to Carrick-on-Suir, community centres, development associations, and benevolent funds. Nationally the money went to the Irish Heart Foundation, four hospitals, and four university colleges.

It would be naïve to suppose that major companies,

multinational or otherwise, make donations of this kind for altruistic reasons. In effect they are buying goodwill, a traditional if somewhat heavy-handed public relations exercise.

Efforts to placate John Hanrahan were less successful. Entries in the Red Book show that humans and animals were in very bad health over this period, with coughing, weeping, running from the nose, vomiting, and general debility.

□

Selina woke with a blinding headache at three o'clock on the morning of 17 September. Dr Kathleen Roche-Nagle told her to go straightaway to the Infirmary Hospital, where she remained for seven days—her third hospital admission in 1982. After a series of tests in Waterford she was transferred to the Mater Hospital, Dublin, for further tests. Some days later she was told she could go home, and she left the hospital for a visit to the city with her sister. While there Selina collapsed and had to be rushed back to the Mater; it was then she consulted Professor Éamon de Valera, a gynaecologist at the Mater, who decided she would have to have immediate gynaecological surgery, suspecting cancer. "I can't guarantee anything, I'm afraid," Professor de Valera told John Hanrahan. "Generally speaking an operation is nothing to worry about, but in her case there are complications. We can hope for the best."

His mother was in hospital undergoing tests at the same time, and Hanrahan was more than ever convinced that the whole combination of circumstances was due to the spectre of Merck, Sharp and Dohme. He felt he had to take the matter further, and that evening he asked his brother-in-law David McBride to go with him to see the Minister for Health, Dr Michael Woods. It was Saturday 9 October. They drove to the minister's home and told him the story. Woods decided the matter needed prompt attention and asked Dr James Walsh, a senior official in the Department of Health, to visit South Tipperary on Monday.

At lunch-time the following Monday Dr Walsh arrived at Ballycurkeen with Dr de Souza. There to meet them was a group of some two dozen people, including John Hanrahan, Tom de Lacy, and Dr Rory Finegan. The remainder were farmers and other residents. Much of the time was taken up with the group recounting their experience of emissions. They raised the subject of the biological investigation carried out at the request of An Foras Forbartha by TCD Botany School, whose report had been leaked about this time, indicating high levels of pollution in the valley.

Later that evening Hanrahan decided to proceed with a plan to give the issue more widespread publicity. For some weeks he had considered the idea of staging a public slaughter of the worst of his sick animals; as well as concentrating minds this would remove unproductive stock that were costing him money to keep and were unsaleable. He opened a large pit near the gate of the farm and prepared to stage the event the following Saturday, 16 October.

It was the action of a man who had reached the point of desperation. Medical and veterinary bills were formidable, as were the costs of the legal case; but the biggest expense was feeding and maintaining unproductive animals. As he faced another winter the feed bill for the previous year was still unpaid. A critical point had arrived when Avonmore Co-op withheld his milk cheque for August to offset against his feed bill. His outstanding debt to the co-op was over £100,000. But Avonmore's name was bound to arise if Hanrahan held a public slaughter. Questions would be asked about the safety of milk and meat from the area, and Avonmore's milk and dairy products would come under suspicion.

The IFA were also concerned at the damage it could do to the reputation of food products originating in the area, which helps to explain why the local branch were slow to get involved. Mary Hanrahan had written in July to the IFA national president, Dónal Cashman, saying she was appalled and sickened at this lack of support. "When a strike takes place in a factory and an injustice has been done to workers," she told the court, "most of the workers strike, with the authority of the union behind them. I had been subscribing to the IFA for many years; I felt if they couldn't do it, they should press someone who could do it."

Earlier the IFA had sought details of Hanrahan's losses, but they were not made available, on the same grounds on which this information was withheld from everyone else. Cashman wrote back to Mary in August asking again for details of the losses. She said the information could only be got through their solicitor. This episode soured relations in the run-up to the public slaughtering encounter; nevertheless, the day before the planned event the Hanrahans were invited to Dublin to meet Hugh Ryan, deputy president, and other members of the organisation. They were told of a meeting the IFA had had that morning with the Taoiseach, Charles Haughey, where the matter was raised. A further meeting was arranged with the Minister for Agriculture, Brian Lenihan, to try to avert the slaughter.

John and Mary Hanrahan met Lenihan with a number of IFA officials that afternoon. Lenihan wondered what the benefit would be of a public slaughtering. Hanrahan said it was a measure of his impatience at official inaction, an attempt to draw attention to the gravity of his situation, which he felt was being ignored and had been minimised in the reports so far produced by Government agencies. Lenihan said he was expecting his own official report the following Tuesday. Hanrahan and his mother agreed to meet the minister again when the report was available, and to postpone the killing.

Hanrahan also met the management of Avonmore Co-op about his account. It was agreed that they would resume payment for his milk and would freeze interest on his outstanding animal feed bill.

In the meantime Merck pursued the issue on the legal front. On Friday 22 October the company's solicitors filed an affidavit for a High Court order restraining Hanrahan from publicising the slaughter of his animals. "In the event that the Plaintiffs proceed to slaughter any of the animals in the presence of RTE cameras or the members of the press, the consequent publicity will seriously prejudice the fair trial of this action."

The slaughtering did not go ahead, but Hanrahan had learnt something about public pressure: he had learnt that it works. At the end of October he arranged to have the TCD report read to a packed meeting in Carrick-on-Suir, largely farmers, including the former IFA president TJ Maher, a number of prominent people from Avonmore Co-op, and some Merck personnel.

The meeting did not go entirely Hanrahan's way. There were searching questions from the Merck people on the TCD report's findings, and inconclusive debate about why the factory staff were apparently not affected by emissions. From this point on the IFA took a decidedly less prominent role in the Hanrahan case, and the tide of local farming opinion, already divided, began to turn against him. Only trusty neighbours like Rockett and Callanan kept faith.

But the Hanrahans did not give up. In early November they acquired the full-time services of a biologist, Dr Geoffrey Buck, one of the authors of the TCD report. Buck's first task was to take samples for analysis from two cows slaughtered on the farm by Tom de Lacy. One of the cows had severe breathing distress and the other had difficulty controlling her movements and had wasted badly. Part of a kidney from one of the cows was sent for examination by Dr John Peterkin of Portsmouth Polytechnic. It was found to have a trace of a substance like amitriptyline hydrochloride—an anti-depressant, one of the finished products at Ballydine—an unconfirmed finding later disputed by Merck witnesses.

☐

On the evening of Saturday 6 November 1982 John Hanrahan noticed a bad smell, which got worse as rain set in. He did not make a complaint, as relationships with the factory and the council had reached a low ebb. The following morning he woke with a pain in his chest; he was more than usually tired and listless and was unable to work his normal day. He consulted Professor Muiris Fitzgerald, and two days later he was admitted to St Vincent's Private Clinic in Dublin for a further set of tests.

The same day Selina had been discharged from hospital after her surgery and had gone to recuperate with her sister in England. She returned to their rented house in Piltown in mid-December to find a new set of entries awaiting inclusion in the Red Book.

The last animal to die in 1982 was a calf on the day before Christmas Eve. So the year ended as it had begun, with animals dying and with human sickness. The recorded death list for the year came to forty animals, only slightly fewer than 1981. Selina had spent three months in hospital, John a month, and Mary two weeks. Six technical reports had been produced, the Taoiseach and two other ministers had been consulted, and the case was rapidly acquiring national notoriety.

7

REPORTS

In July 1982 the Minister for Agriculture, Brian Lenihan, had assigned a team headed by Dr Mark Lynch to investigate the Hanrahan case on his behalf. Lynch's first visit to South Tipperary was inauspicious. He and two colleagues spent three days in the area in mid-July. They met officials of the county council, personnel from Merck, Sharp and Dohme, Dr Jamieson of An Foras Forbartha, Pat Crowe of the Kilkenny laboratory, and an officer of the Meteorological Service.

On 14 July Lynch and his colleagues met Michael English, who gave them an outline of the problems. They asked him to get some additional information from the Hanrahans, but they did not visit the farm. John Hanrahan was less than impressed, and his already shaken trust in the official attitude was further weakened.

"We had intended also seeking a meeting at that time with the Hanrahans," Lynch told the court, "but decided against doing so on foot of advice from the CAO [chief agricultural officer] that there was a newspaper reporter on the farm at the time. Our instructions were to conduct an informal investigation and hence at that time we did not visit the farm." It seemed a rather weak excuse. Early in September John Hanrahan and his mother called to Lynch's office in Dublin. They discussed his investigation, and Lynch said he had now read all the reports. After some discussion Mary Hanrahan invited him to visit the farm. A date was fixed for the end of September.

Towards the middle of 1982 public interest in the case was aroused by the simultaneous arrival of results from a number of different studies. The first was a report of tests on soil, herbage and manure from the farm carried out at the request of Michael English by An Foras Talúntais. A team of scientists had visited the farm in April 1982 and had discussed the problems with Hanrahan and collected samples for analysis. "The results of this study indicate that deficiencies or excess of the elements tested for are not responsible for the problems on Mr Hanrahan's farm." The report did not rule out the possibility that organic compounds or other chemicals, not tested for, could be contributing to the problems. It found that soil levels of the major plant nutrients, phosphorus and potassium, were low and were almost certainly limiting grass growth. Some of the herbage samples were also low in these two elements for the time of year.

In August 1982 Dr Ian Jamieson produced a report on his second study, covering the period April 1981 to April 1982. The main conclusion was that average concentrations of vapours in the air around Ballydine complied with air quality standards at all times. Sulphur dioxide and smoke from the Merck boiler stack were not causing unacceptably high concentrations at ground level, and vapours at the mouth of the scrubber stack complied with pollution standards on each occasion they were measured. (A scrubber is a device designed to neutralise toxic gases and vapours by spraying them with water or sodium hydroxide before releasing them to the air.)

Thioanisole was not detected, but three organic chemicals not normally found in rural areas were found in the air though at well below accepted danger levels. The only local source of these organics was the Merck factory. One of these was monochlorobenzene, a highly dangerous substance used extensively at the plant. On 9 July 1981 Jamieson found it in the gas emerging from the scrubber stack, while at the same time a significant increase was measured at Hanrahan's farm. But this finding was somewhat devalued when equally high levels were measured at the farm after the process in which monochlorobenzene was used was apparently discontinued at the factory.

In passing, the report mentioned the results of scrubber stack emission tests supplied by the factory showing that during May and June 1980 the planning permission level for hydrochloric acid had been exceeded. (The planning permission level is not to be confused with the "threshold limit value"—the minimum level at which vapours would be irritating—which is not a statutory limit but a standard recommended by industrial health bodies.) The admission that the planning level was exceeded would later attract considerable attention during the High Court case.

Jamieson acknowledged that Ballydine residents were sometimes subjected to short exposures of factory vapours that might have an unpleasant odour or might irritate the skin and eyes, and that it was unlikely in future they would be entirely free of such occurrences. However, he reported that the levels of pollutants measured could not have seriously affected health or caused the cattle deaths at Hanrahan's farm.

His main recommendation was that the animal health problems be fully investigated by veterinary and other authorities; but issues were raised in the report that left room for a more disturbing interpretation of what was happening. Central to these was the possibility that very high short-term concentrations of vapour were occurring, which Jamieson's equipment was not able to measure and which a daily average would disguise. Acknowledging this as a possible key to the Ballydine mystery, Jamieson recommended that emissions be monitored by more complex equipment. It should be fully automatic and be able to record continuously and indicate peaks in concentration. Such an instrument was never acquired, although Jamieson repeated the recommendation again and again. He also recommended that the exhaust gas from the solvent incinerator be examined in detail. It would be sixteen months before this was attempted.

This report was a serious disappointment to Hanrahan. It was saying in effect that whatever problems he and his family and his animals were having they were not caused by the factory emissions. On the contrary, they might be due to factors internal to the farm that needed investigation.

On Monday 27 September 1982 Dr Mark Lynch and two of his colleagues arrived at Ballycurkeen. There to meet them were the Hanrahan family, Tom de Lacy, Tommy Rockett, and a number of other local farmers, including Michael Slattery, the IFA chairman for Munster. Chairing the meeting was Tom Menton, the family solicitor, and in attendance also were Dr de Souza, the county medical officer; Dr Denis Flanagan, Mary Hanrahan's doctor; Michael English; Dave Hurley, the retired chief agricultural officer; Dr Rory Finegan, the Canadian biologist, Dr Bill Murray, a chemical engineer from Cork RTC; and Dr Paul Dowding of TCD.

Relations by now had deteriorated further. The Hanrahans were unhappy with the results of the Jamieson report, and they believed that the results of the TCD biological study were being withheld. In fact the parties appeared to have approached the meeting with different objectives. Since it arose from Mary Hanrahan's invitation to Lynch, the Hanrahans felt it should be their agenda; and their priority at the time was to get the results of the TCD study, to have monitoring resumed, and to get their health complaints dealt with. Lynch and the Department of Agriculture team had a different perception.

On 29 July Michael English had received a letter from a department official with a list of eight questions about the farm. He passed the letter on to John Hanrahan, and Tom Menton responded on his behalf. He included Selina's death list, the number of twins born, milk production records from 1978, an indication of meal fed to the cows, and stock numbers on the farm each year since 1978. The information that remained outstanding included detailed ages of animals, dates of abnormal behaviour, dates of unpleasant odours, animal health symptoms, and veterinary reports on the causes of death. Menton later sent pathology reports on the three cows examined at the veterinary college, but the bulk of the veterinary reports would not be handed over. Details of feed and fertilisers bought were later obtained from Avonmore, along with confirmation of the milk supply records.

In the meantime Lynch arrived at the September meeting looking for information. He was given a general outline of the veterinary problems and a list of dates when animals had suffered from respiratory distress. There were no veterinary reports. In addition to the details already sought, the department now wanted answers to twenty further questions on age, breed, pedigree and culling pattern of the herd, meals fed, fertilisers applied, silage cut, grassland management, and animal health since 1976.

Despite being told that Hanrahan had unusually detailed and comprehensive records, Lynch and his colleagues were given no further information. "We were told that this was information in the context of legal proceedings, could not be provided. It wasn't, in any event."

In view of developments over the previous months it was hardly surprising that Hanrahan's team were suspicious. Legal proceedings had been begun in February, followed by a series of letters from Merck's solicitors seeking, quite legitimately, particulars of the Hanrahans' claim, including veterinary reports. However innocent the conjunction, finding the Department of Agriculture in pursuit of the same information did not inspire confidence in the department, and gave further support to Hanrahan's conspiracy theory.

Tom de Lacy told the meeting he was unhappy to allow meat and milk to be sold from the farm. Lynch agreed to convey the message to the minister, and a week later a letter came from the minister's office saying the only department restrictions on cattle movement related to the tuberculosis and brucellosis eradication schemes.

Intermittently, the September meeting moved to a

discussion of the TCD report. Dr Lynch said he had not seen it, and Dr Dowding, one of the authors, said the report was commissioned by An Foras Forbartha for the county council and until they gave approval it would be improper of him to discuss the findings.

Tom de Lacy wondered why the parties directly and intimately involved could be denied the findings when everybody knew they were available, and became more exasperated as his inquiries were getting no satisfactory response. Eventually he and John Hanrahan left the room. Outside Hanrahan gave him a copy of the report, which he had acquired. The meeting was taken aback when de Lacy returned and slapped the document on the table before them. It was made clear that Dowding was not the source of Hanrahan's copy, but since the report was now available to the meeting, Dowding felt free to participate in the discussion of its contents. The news that the Hanrahans had the report apparently filtered back to the county council and after lunch Lynch was called away. He told them he was going to the county council to be given a copy of the report.

The report dealt with a series of biological investigations by a team of eight people from the college carried out between May and September 1982. The project director was Professor David Richardson of the Botany School, and in charge of different aspects of field operations were Dr Paul Dowding and Dr Geoffrey Buck.

It was perhaps the unambiguous nature of the TCD report that subsequently led to such concern in establishment circles. Although it did not conclusively prove any link, it openly assumed that emissions from the plant could be responsible for the Hanrahans' animal and human health problems. It reported high levels of pollution on the valley sides, including Hanrahan's farm, and elevated levels of bromine, chlorine and sulphur in grass, silage, lichen and hair collected from the farm. Fertiliser and sea spray were not ruled out as contributing factors, but the main emphasis was in considering which Merck chemicals may have been at fault.

It was well known that sulphur was emitted from the Merck boiler stack in the form of sulphur dioxide, but that was dismissed by the TCD team as the cause of that problem. Noting that chlorine compounds can cause respiratory distress, they explored the possibilities. Hydrochloric acid irritates the mucous membranes but has no toxic effect apart from its acidic action. "However," the report said, "very high levels of HCl, released for short periods, may have induced the observed symptoms in the cattle."

It was suggested that a likely source of both bromine and chlorine was the Merck incinerator. If combustion of organic chemicals was not complete, a number of compounds could have been released that would give rise to "burning eyes, coughing, inability to get breath, followed by peri-bronchial oedema, pulmonary congestion."

Like Jamieson, the TCD team also mentioned the possibility that the problems may have been due to a highly toxic organic substance in low concentration which they could not identify. The animal hair analyses would suggest "that the substance concerned may be a toxic compound of bromine and/or chlorine emitted in quantity during the summer of 1981." They recommended further biological studies and "investigations on the nature and quantity of the chlorinated and brominated compounds in the emissions from the Merck, Sharp and Dohme factory at Ballydine." There was no suggestion that factors internal to the Hanrahan farm might have caused their problems.

On the day after the Ballycurkeen meeting the *Irish Times* carried an account by John Armstrong of the findings of the TCD report. No doubt the leaks worried the company, but they also worried county council officials, and led to a crisis meeting. A delegation from the council drove to Dublin to meet some of the authors of the report and Dr Jamieson, who had recommended the study. An assessment of the findings was prepared by Dr Jamieson and Professor Richardson for the following month.

On 15 October Dr Jamieson sent a copy of the assessment

to Jim O'Callaghan, South Tipperary county engineer. "The report of the biological investigations prepared by Trinity College and sent to you in September was an in-house document addressed to An Foras Forbartha and, in view of its nature, unsuited for general distribution ... It is unfortunate that some statements in the report have been quoted—in the press—out of context and without an explanation or understanding of their exact significance." Comments had been made indicating levels of pollution similar to those found in central Dublin. "This does not mean that conditions in Ballydine or central Dublin have been found to be hazardous." The TCD report, he said, found that lichens in the immediate area of the factory had not been killed by pollution, and made it quite clear that the team was unable to determine whether the remarkably high levels of sulphur, chlorine and bromine found in lichens had arisen from natural causes or emissions.

Apart from changing the emphasis of the TCD conclusions, the assessment reported on two further investigations that Jamieson and Richardson had carried out themselves. The first was a comparison of herbage samples from Hanrahan's farm before and after the arrival of the Merck factory. Average values of sulphur, chlorine and bromine were found to be higher in the 1975 samples from the farm than in those measured by TCD in 1982. They argued that, because none of the three elements had increased in the herbage since the factory arrived, the high levels reported by the TCD team came from wind-blown sea spray and fertiliser, with some sulphur from the Merck boiler chimney.

The second investigation was a re-analysis of the samples collected in 1982 by the TCD team. It led them to the conclusion that the bromine values were overestimated by a factor of 1.8 because of faulty technique; but allowing for that mistake, the pattern of bromine peaks remained.

Jamieson and Richardson said the new data did not rule out the possibility that the animal health problem on the farm was caused by "a highly toxic substance emitted in low concentration" but it could also be due to nutritional deficiencies or imbalance, and they recommended that sick animals be transferred to a veterinary station for intensive study. In conclusion they felt that causes of the animal health problems "other than air pollution-induced, should be examined before proceeding with sophisticated and costly investigations of air quality."

So the pressure was back on Hanrahan. After a respite following the findings of the TCD report, once again he and his farm management were to become the focus of investigation. He was convinced that had the TCD report not been leaked, the contents would have been suppressed. The strong conclusions of the TCD report had been watered down, he believed, in deference to the wishes of the company and the county council.

☐

After he had gone to work full-time for the Hanrahans, Geoffrey Buck, an intense man with persistence to rival that of John Hanrahan, became involved in almost all aspects of the family's problems, and his findings obviously worried the Merck team. It was important for the defence to discredit the TCD report. They recruited one of Buck's former lecturers, Dr Denis Brown, a specialist in plant physiology who supervised Buck's doctorate at Bristol University.

Peter Shanley, one of the barristers for Merck, referred Brown to Buck's further studies concluding that the lichen population had declined between 1982 and 1985. "I want to ask you, in relation to that study, whether you believe those conclusions are warranted or not?"

"On the basis of the evidence available I don't think they are justifiable." Buck's study area was too small, too many of the locations were chosen on Hanrahan's side of the factory, and different species of lichen were being compared from locations that were not the same in both studies. To use inadequate data could only produce ambiguous conclusions.

It was the hair studies undertaken by Buck that threw up the most disturbing results. He had outlined in the TCD report how cattle hair on Hanrahan's farm showed levels of bromine and chlorine several times higher than cattle hair from Co Meath. Moreover, hair from the tail of a pony on the farm showed peaks of these two elements occurring in the summer of 1981, when the Hanrahans' problems were at their worst. The implication was that the levels of these elements in the animal's blood were high at that time. But Buck had gone further. He had also tested a sample of hair from Mary Hanrahan's head. It showed a peak of chlorine and bromine at approximately the same time in 1981 as the peak recorded in the pony. He concluded that this ruled out food as the source of the elements; therefore, it had to be the water or the air. There was no evidence of high levels of these two elements in the water. That left the air.

In 1983 he repeated the hair study on the pony, which confirmed the result. As the hair had grown with the tail, the bromine peak had moved with it. He did a further study on the same pony in 1985 showing a new peak for bromine.

Brown pointed out some inconsistencies in Buck's results from the hair studies and said he had insufficient information to make any useful observation.

"You don't dispute the bromine peaks in the tails, in the hairs?" Dermot Gleeson asked him finally.

"I am aware that bromine has been associated with hairs," Brown replied. "When you use the term 'in the hairs' I would not be necessarily willing to agree with you."

"The bromine peaks identified by Dr Buck—you don't dispute their existence?"

"I have no reason to believe they are not adequately analysed."

In attempting to explain the peaks of chlorine and bromine he measured in hair, Buck made the assumption that the elements came from the Merck factory, and identified the manufacture of sulindac as the possible source. His research revealed that there was more than one way of making sulindac; some involved the use of bromine and some did not. But the Hanrahan team could not force the company to disclose the exact chemical formula they used, on the grounds that this information was commercially privileged. "The sulindac campaigns [manufacturing cycles] appeared to conform approximately to the peak of the bromine and chlorine found in the pony tail," Buck said. "We know that the chloroform is involved in the sulindac process. On this basis I assume that bromine is also involved . . . The chlorine and the bromine produce peaks at the same time along the line of the pony tail. Certainly several of the patents would lead me to believe that bromine is a possible contributor to the sulindac process. Again I think I have got six or seven separate patents and I think two or three of them involved bromine."

But both Declan Buckley, Merck general manager, and Dr David MacSweeney, Merck head of technical services, denied categorically that the factory used bromine in the manufacture of sulindac. MacSweeney went on to explain that sulindac is made in seven stages, only the final three of which are carried out in Ballydine. None of the imported materials contained bromine, and none of the final three steps involved its use. They had used three different types of bromide at different stages in the factory up to 1978 and after December 1981. Later he told Dermot Gleeson that a bromide was used in the making of amitriptyline hydrochloride up to 1978, and at that stage it was disposed of to the waste treatment plant—not by incineration. Merck documents show that amitriptyline hydrochloride was made at the factory in the middle of 1981, but apparently without the use of bromine.

Bromine had been found to occur at high levels in human and animal hair in 1981, in animal hair again in 1983 and 1984, and in lichens and herbage in 1982. Silage made from grass cut in the summer of 1981 had twice the level found in 1975 herbage. That silage was the only 1981 herbage tested for bromine, so it is possible that, had more tests been done in 1981, the levels would have been higher than 1975 also. Finally, excessive amounts of bromine were detected in John Hanrahan's blood and urine at the end of 1982. But according to Merck evidence bromine was not used in the factory at the critical times, and the evidence also appeared to rule out the possibility that bromine included in a bromide (though not used in the process in 1981) was disposed of by incineration at that time or later. The mystery of bromine peaks remained unsolved.

□

Dr Mark Lynch and his colleagues submitted an interim report to the Minister for Agriculture on 19 October 1982. This was never released officially, even in its final form produced eighteen months later. Compiled from data made available to the team during various meetings, including the one at Hanrahan's house in September, it was "based on the assumption that the problems occurring could result from emissions from the M.S.D. plant."

Before considering the data collected, the team gave what they described as a summary of the various studies already available. Summarising the conclusions of Dr Jamieson's first report in 1980, they said that levels of thioanisole and toluene measured were "acceptably low." In fact, while reporting low concentrations, Dr Jamieson had said Merck should be advised that "the presence of thioanisole vapours is unacceptable."

Dealing with Jamieson's second report the Lynch team quoted his main conclusion, that average levels of acid and organics in the Ballydine air were within accepted standards; but they failed to mention monochlorobenzene, detected simultaneously in factory emissions and at Hanrahan's farm. Since the factory was the only possible source of this unusual and dangerous substance, the finding would seem to have warranted inclusion. The summary also failed to mention Jamieson's observation that the factory had exceeded its planning permission level for emissions of hydrochloric acid during May and June of 1980. In fact Lynch did not become aware of it until the High Court hearing.

On 10 November 1981 Tom Coffey, an engineer in the Department of the Environment, and Jim O'Callaghan, South Tipperary county engineer, visited the Merck factory and a number of farms in the area, including Hanrahan's. Their report to the minister was not published, but Lynch and his colleagues summarised the contents. The main conclusion was that the Merck incinerator when in operation gave rise to lachrymation, irritation, and some respiratory difficulties. They also reported that Hanrahan's was the only farm in the area claiming serious animal and human health problems; O'Meara and Rockett had problems of a lesser nature. This report to the Minister for the Environment was the first formal acknowledgement that the operation of the Merck incinerator was related to these problems. It would be two years before it was studied again, and four years before serious operating faults were uncovered.

The Lynch team pointed to deficiencies and excesses of certain nutrients on the farm reported by An Foras Talúntais in 1982, but did not include the main conclusion, that "deficiencies or excess of elements tested for are not responsible for the problems on Hanrahan's farm." Rather than summarising the TCD report they appeared to concentrate on the interpretation of its findings by Jamieson and Richardson.

The TCD leaf yeast study had indicated heavy airborne pollution on elevated sites in the valley, including the Hanrahan farm. But the Lynch team maintained that this interpretation was "untenable in the context of meteorological conditions if the M.S.D. plant is the source." In fact a meteorological report for the Lynch team came to the opposite conclusion. It was prepared by Liam Burke of the Meteorological Service, following a tour of the valley with Lynch and his colleagues in July. This report said that, with the Hanrahan farm on rising ground north-east of the factory, "it is fairly certain . . . that the belt of trees near the farm produces turbulent eddies on the lee side in moderate winds. When the winds are blowing from the factory towards the farm these eddies would assist in bringing down any pollution at higher levels."

Of the TCD animal hair study the Lynch summary says "the methodology used was deficient" and therefore no conclusions could be drawn. But even Jamieson and Richardson's assessment casts no doubt on the merits of the hair analysis. Their criticism applied only to the technique used in estimating bromine levels in herbage.

Having presented their summary of other studies, the Lynch team went on to report some studies of their own. The main body of the report was the outcome of an informal investigation by the team using information from a variety of sources. These included John Hanrahan, Merck, and the many state organisations that had taken an interest in the case.

They first looked at the possible impact of Merck emissions, and at this stage quoted Liam Burke's meteorological conclusion, that emissions could under certain conditions impinge on the Hanrahan farm and not on others. Referring to low levels of pollutants on the farm they said that accidental spillages and operator errors led occasionally to uncontrollable plant emissions of a nuisance nature. There was evidence that emissions from the plant incinerator caused irritation and weeping more frequently. Nevertheless, the Lynch team said, no direct link had been established between the operation of the plant and the serious animal health condition on the farm, although materials from the incinerator might be contributing to the respiratory problems. The possibility of unidentified emissions contributing could not be discounted. They recommended further study of the incinerator and emissions from other parts of the factory.

Accepting that a serious animal health problem existed on the farm, Lynch and his team went on to consider the animal conditions individually and to conclude that most of them were not abnormal. The main recommendation declared, "It is pointless to expend further State resources on investigation of the problem" until a list of information was provided by Hanrahan and his advisers. At the top of the list were the reports of vets and consultants employed by Hanrahan privately. Added to these was detailed farm management information such as volume of milk fed to calves, age, lactation length, calving dates, breeding records, animals bought and sold, meal feeding, grazing rotation, fertiliser application, crop records, and a comprehensive record of the animal health problems.

"Your conclusion," Dermot Gleeson read from the Lynch report—"you said that 'it is possible that factors internal to the farm could be the major cause of the problems experienced.' You were turning the blame on Hanrahan for the way his land was managed. That is what you reported to him [the Minister for Agriculture] in 1982. You had nothing to say about Merck, Sharp and Dohme chemicals?"

"At that stage we had not had the benefit of a detailed investigation of the processes in the Merck, Sharp and Dohme factory . . . I have on several occasions stated that any scientific investigations of the problem of the Hanrahan farm would be totally dependent on specific quantification of the problems reported on the farm. Having done that it would be foolish and silly not to review and evaluate the management of the farm with a view to discounting any problems that were indeed specified and quantified but could be explained on that basis . . ."

Apart from the findings of the vets and private consultants, the Lynch team could have collected most of the outstanding information themselves in a few days' research on the farm, had there been enough good will between the parties. But John Hanrahan felt that the investigating team's purpose was to accumulate information about his farm management that they would use against him. At great expense he had engaged consultants to carry out the kind of investigation he felt should be the responsibility of the Department of Agriculture, the county council, and other public bodies, and now they wanted access to whatever information he might have uncovered. Worse still, Hanrahan believed the findings would be made available to Merck, at a time when he and his advisers were unable to obtain the most basic information about the materials used in the factory and the processes carried on there.

Lynch concluded that their investigation was seriously hampered by the lack of information on the farm, in contrast to the ready supply of data from Merck. But whatever the quality of information supplied by Merck to the Lynch team, even the court was unable to force the company to disclose details of its processes.

On 10 November 1982 the county manager, Tom Rice, presented the council members with what he described as a synopsis and assessment of investigations carried out in the Ballydine district in the period 1975–82. It was prepared by the county engineer, with a short preamble by Rice himself, in which he declared that the results of the investigations "do not indicate any breach of the terms and conditions on which the plant is entitled to operate and, therefore, the necessity for corrective action or enforcement proceedings does not arise." As would later become apparent, that statement was not correct.

O'Callaghan emphasised that no link had been established between the serious animal health problem and the operations of Merck. Equally there was no conclusive evidence that factors internal to the farm were responsible. He said four of the reports had referred to the possibility that unidentified and undetected toxic emissions from the plant could have contributed. "There is, in my opinion, no evidence to substantiate these speculative opinions . . ." But in his synopsis of Jamieson's second report O'Callaghan might have drawn attention to the detection of monochlorobenzene. If such a lethal substance was detected once, was it not at least worth considering whether it, or more dangerous compounds, were candidates for the mystery toxic emission?

Like the Lynch team, O'Callaghan chose to report Jamieson and Richardson's assessment of the TCD report rather than the report itself. He pointed out that the yeast counts taken in the elevated locations in the valley indicated pollution levels as high as or higher than in central Dublin, but they were within safety limits. He said that other industries in the valley, in addition to Merck, were likely to have contributed to the pollution.

On the lichen study O'Callaghan noted their finding "a comparatively rich flora close to the plant." He chose to emphasise that the TCD authors did not define the relative contribution of emissions, fertilisers and sea spray to the high level of some elements measured. They had concluded that there was clear evidence that the lichens were absorbing sulphur from Merck emissions.

These studies had shown, O'Callaghan said, that levels of all the elements measured were higher in 1975 than in 1982. He might have used the opportunity to conclude that the elemental content of herbage, therefore, was unlikely to have had any bearing on the animal health problem. As he did point out later, this was the conclusion reached by the Foras Talúntais team in 1982. However, O'Callaghan continued, the Lynch report concluded that elemental levels "internal to the farm" could be "the major causes of the problems experienced."

Turning to the TCD animal hair study, O'Callaghan repeated for the council members the opinion of the Lynch report that faulty technique was used. And when it came to assessing the Lynch report itself, O'Callaghan simply repeated its conclusions.

Looking at official attitudes as seen through the 1982 reports, John Hanrahan might be forgiven for believing that the establishment was content to give the benefit of the doubt to Merck. The TCD report had pointed the finger definitely at the plant as the most likely source of the animal and human health problems; but had it not been leaked, it is doubtful if its findings would have appeared in public in their original form. The case against Merck was by no means proved, but the Jamieson and TCD reports between them raised enough reasonable doubt about the company's innocence to warrant a public demand for closer scrutiny.

But the effect of all the reports and assessments released in 1982 was to direct the demand for such scrutiny against Hanrahan himself. Press statements from Merck began to emphasise that Hanrahan's experience was unique. Only one farmer was having trouble. In a small and vulnerable community like South Tipperary, it is perhaps not surprising that a more benign attitude will be taken to a company employing 250 people than to a big farmer with an abrasive manner and a poorly defined grievance. The Hanrahan family's ordeal was to continue.

8

THE POLITICAL ARENA

By the beginning of 1983 the situation in Ballydine and Ballycurkeen was causing a great deal of concern to the new Government headed by Garret FitzGerald that had taken office in November 1982. Avril Doyle, Fine Gael deputy for Wexford, had been appointed Minister of State for Finance. In early March she spoke to the Hanrahans about the possibility of a veterinary investigation, to be supervised by FitzGerald's friend and former Government colleague Justin Keating, who had extensive vererinary qualifications. They were happy with the choice, but the plan came to nothing—because, as FitzGerald said later, a number of civil servants objected, and the Government rejected it. The last chance to avoid a confrontation may have been missed.

After a discussion on 25 March it was decided that Liam Kavanagh, one of the four Labour Party members in the Government, would co-ordinate a study involving the Ministers for Health, Industry and Energy, Agriculture, and the Environment. A committee was set up and given a mandate to call on all the resources of the state in a serious attempt to get to the root of the problem.

The Lynch report, submitted to the Department of Agriculture in October 1982, declared that it was pointless expending further state resources until all existing evidence and the reports of Hanrahan's consultants were provided. In pursuit of this objective the department delegated a new team of experts to investigate. On the afternoon of 25 January 1983 Pat Crowe from the Kilkenny laboratory, two other department vets and a nutritionist arrived on the farm. They spent a number of hours in the house discussing the problem with de Lacy and Hanrahan.

According to Hanrahan the point of their inquiries was to ascertain the nature and results of the investigations being undertaken privately by his own scientific team. It was not an unreasonable approach, following the recommendations of the Lynch report; but it was refused. By now the Hanrahan side was not prepared to accept the department's good faith. In any case they felt it was up to the department to carry out its own scientific study, irrespective of other findings. Whatever the merits of the first Lynch report, it did not claim to have undertaken independent scientific tests; it was little more than a review of previous studies.

On 1 March the county council disconnected the public water supply to Hanrahan's farm, on the grounds that he had refused to pay £1,800 arrears of water rates. He was trying to force the council to implement the recommendations in Dr Jamieson's report. This left him with over 370 animals in winter housing with no drinking water. After representations to the Minister for the Environment, Dick Spring, the supply was reconnected. (In 1986 the water was cut off again, and Hanrahan decided to find an independent supply by drilling a well on the farm.)

After midnight on 9 April 1983 John Hanrahan asked Eddie Keating, a partner in Tom de Lacy's veterinary practice, to come and help him with a cow that was having difficulty calving. When Keating arrived he noticed an unpleasant burning sensation. They found it irritating to nose and throat, and the animals in the shed began to cough. After a short while Keating began to feel unwell and said the conditions were unsafe to work in. Before leaving he suggested that Hanrahan report it to the factory.

By then it was 1.45 a.m., but Hanrahan decided to telephone the county engineer, Jim O'Callaghan, at his home. A few days later he had a letter from the county secretary, pointing out that the factory was not in operation that night, that the wind was from the opposite direction, and that in any case, on being told of the complaint, factory personnel had visited the farm and detected nothing. This incident was reported in June in a long feature on the Ballydine problems in *Magill*. The Merck log of Hanrahan's complaint showed that the factory was in fact operating that night, making sulindac and two other products.

An interim report was produced by the Kavanagh committee on 7 July 1983. Its findings were never published, and there was no final report. Much of it was taken up in summarising the findings of previous studies, with, occasionally, the committee's own interpretation of those findings. They went to the county council and Merck, but did not visit the farm. Hitherto unreported investigations were also included. At a number of public meetings in April and May 1981 the county medical officer, Dr de Souza, had invited people with respiratory problems in the Ballydine area to contact him. Only six families responded; according to Kavanagh, in no case did the people coming forward display acute respiratory symptoms. The report also revealed that following Dr James Walsh's visit to the area in October 1982 it was decided to carry out an epidemiological health study. The study was still in progress in 1983, but in the meantime no significant findings had emerged.

Samples of milk from the area analysed by the State Laboratory in February 1983 at the request of Dr de Souza were found to have increased levels of bromide compared with a sample taken from outside the area. No significance was attached to these results, as they were not replicated in subsequent tests. In any case by 1983 it was idle to wonder what the levels in milk might have been in 1981 or 1982, when the TCD team had detected elevated bromine levels in their investigation.

The Kavanagh team reiterated the Lynch conclusion that the emissions from the factory were unlikely to cause problems. Kavanagh went on to include the results of a survey of the factory in April 1983 by inspectors from the Department of Labour. But the inspectors were no more successful in getting access to complete information on the factory than the Department of Agriculture had been on the farm. "Access to much of the information required is difficult because of the lack of provision in safety, health and welfare legislation to allow the Industrial Inspectorate to have access to research, design, process and occupational health information available to the company.

"Within the confines of the information made available to the Industrial Inspectorate, the processes did not suggest the production of any by-products with more aggressive properties than those already known in the factory." It was not a very comforting conclusion when the previous paragraph had said, "The information gathered on plant chemicals indicates a wide range of hazards, including flammability, explosibility, toxicity and sensitising properties." The management of the health hazards in the firm "appeared to be satisfactory considering the nature of the industry."

The report did not please Garret FitzGerald. In a letter to Kavanagh dated 19 July 1983 he raised sixty-one specific questions and pointed out a number of inconsistencies in the document. He noted from the report that "despite the extreme urgency of the latter, as discussed at Government at the time when it was decided to establish this inquiry, in place of an independent investigation, the committee did not hold its first meeting until five weeks after the date of the Government decision." He wondered why it should have taken three-and-a-half months to produce a document of twenty-five pages.

With a Dublin city background and an ambitious agenda, it would be surprising if Garret FitzGerald, after just four months in office, showed more than passing interest in the animal health problems of one Tipperary farmer unless he thought the case had more far-reaching implications. The answer may lie in the little word "dioxin." Almost all the reports mentioned the possibility of an unknown and undetected toxic substance being responsible for the problems reported. This was a prime suspect.

Tetrachlorodibenzodioxin is the most toxic compound yet created. It is a member of the family of dioxins, which contains seventy-five compounds, not all equally toxic. A family of first cousins, the furans, has 135 members, also with varying degrees of toxicity.

In 1983 the two thousand inhabitants of the town of Times Beach, Missouri, were evacuated when dioxin was detected at approximately one part per billion in the soil around the town. A haulier paid to dispose of chemical waste had mixed it with waste oil and sprayed the mixture on gravel roads to keep the dust down. But when the local river burst its banks the flood spread the deadly poison around. It caused the death of thousands of birds and animals, and the people fled. Nobody has been back there since.

At Love Canal near Niagara Falls, thousands of people were evacuated when dioxin residues at a somewhat lower concentration were found in soil under their houses. The residues had leaked from a nearby dump site.

In Midland, Michigan, the Dow Chemical Company was forced to pave over its factory site after an investigation in 1983 found the soil to be heavily contaminated with dioxin. Dow is the company that developed and manufactured the infamous Agent Orange, which gave dioxin its greatest notoriety as a defoliant in Vietnam. This compound is suspected of causing cancer and birth defects among the Vietnamese people and among US troops who had been exposed to it, although direct cause and effect has not been proved.

Neither was a direct link found at Seveso in Italy, where on 10 July 1976 a faulty valve in a chemical plant led to a release of dioxin into the air. Three hundred acres in the immediate vicinity of the plant were evacuated, and there is said to be a legacy of abortions and birth defects, such as spina bifida.

Perhaps a certain morbid fascination has grown up

around dioxin. The tiny concentration at which it has been found to be poisonous is mind-boggling; it is thought to be toxic as soon as any level whatsoever can be measured, and possibly sooner. The classic symptom of dioxin poisoning in humans is a skin irritation and rash known as chloracne. Test animals develop dry, scaly skin, hair loss, abortions, and birth defects. Other effects include liver or kidney abnormalities or a wasting syndrome.

Dioxins can be created when chemicals with a ring structure, like benzene, monochlorobenzene, or toluene, are burned at certain temperatures in the presence of compounds containing chlorine, such as chloroform. The potential for such a combination of circumstances existed at the Merck plant in Ballydine.

A week after he received FitzGerald's letter Kavanagh responded in a letter almost the length of the report itself, giving detailed answers to the Taoiseach's questions. It listed fifteen different reports and studies carried out by a variety of organisations. It did not include, however, reports on the farm by the county council's vet, Peter Dougan, as requested by FitzGerald. According to Kavanagh's letter the county manager had indicated that "Dougan's report was general and was delivered verbally." In fact Dougan delivered two written reports, which were quite specific. They were not uncovered until the High Court case in 1985, when Dougan himself testified to their content. His account was entirely supportive of Hanrahan's case, and all the more convincing in view of his position.

Early on FitzGerald raised the question of access to information about the factory operation. How could the report be so sure that allegations of emissions like dioxin were untenable when information on processes had not been made available by the company? Kavanagh's answer resorted to the Lynch conclusion that the information provided was sufficient to "permit of the characterisation in chemical terms of potential emissions" from the plant. The information was detailed enough to show that the reaction processes "are unlikely to produce such compounds." He said the information not made available to the Department of Labour inspectors related only to an assessment of hazards to the workers.

"Is it the case," FitzGerald had asked, "that there is no power to require the release of such information and that it is possible for a factory to operate in a manner that might be dangerous to health without any power existing to enable the State to establish whether or not this is the case?" More specifically FitzGerald had dwelt in detail on the incinerator and the kind of chemical compounds it was burning. "If the compounds contain bromine, fluorine or chlorine, is it the case that if combustion were incomplete, a mixture of chlorinated or brominated organic compounds would be emitted? Would this raise the serious question of the possibility of dioxins and furans?"

Kavanagh's answer displayed none of the alarm that might be expected at such a suggestion. "Since tetrahydro-furan is used as a solvent in the plant, it is conceivable that furans could be emitted from the incinerator when there is incomplete combustion. However, in the Department of the Environment's view, it is unlikely that dioxin would be generated in the incinerator." While lung damage was reported on the Hanrahan farm, Kavanagh pointed out that this can be caused by irritants, sensitising agents, micro-organisms, parasites, and viruses. "The limited veterinary information available is not sufficient to sustain speculation that the observed damage results from exposure to dioxins."

Dealing with a question from FitzGerald about other farms in the Ballydine area, Kavanagh said veterinary practitioners were not reporting any unusual animal health problems, and no requests for help had been made to the Kilkenny laboratory. Copper and iodine deficiency were long-standing features of the dairy herds in the area and might explain some of the conditions afflicting the Hanrahan herd. He did not explain how the surrounding herds could have remained immune to such conditions.

"Given that it has been stated repeatedly that Hanrahans and their legal advisers would cooperate if an independent person or team of experts investigated the problem," FitzGerald had asked, "how could the Government be expected to justify a failure to undertake such an inquiry, on the sole grounds of the non-cooperation of one individual, if it eventually transpired that there was in fact a serious problem?"

Hanrahan was the main complainant, Kavanagh replied, and the expense of such a study could not be justified unless all other avenues were exhausted. "Were the necessary access provided, it is likely that the cause of the problems could be identified, in which case the outside study would be unnecessary."

It could not be stated that the factory was not producing toxic substances, but in such an event "both animal and human health problems would be expected to be widespread in the area and workers in and around the plant would be the most likely to be the first to be exposed."

This argument had a rather jaded ring to it by the end of July 1983.

9

VETERINARY INVESTIGATIONS

"When I got out of the car that morning the first thing I noticed was this irritation down my chest that I got through 1982."

Ger Clancy was describing his arrival at Ballycurkeen on the morning of 12 October 1983 to do the compulsory annual test for TB and brucellosis. It was just after 7.00 a.m. There were 368 cattle to be tested altogether, including cows, younger cattle, and calves. It would be a long day.

"The first cows to be subjected to the test were the cows that had been milked, and what was very obvious that day was the extent of the coughing in the adult cows. It was most difficult to carry out the procedure, because the cows were coughing that much . . . I'd be shouting at the cows to urge them to go up the chute, and I remember when you'd be shouting you'd be taking deep breaths of air, and I remember having to stop doing that, my throat was burning so much. I was getting sorer and sorer, and this irritation continued into my throat until eleven o'clock or eleven thirty. I wasn't checking it to see when it went away, but I noticed about eleven thirty the sensation of burning eased off considerably. What became obvious then, the cows had stopped coughing as well, and I remember that was when I really became fully convinced beyond all doubt that the coughing in the cows was associated with the irritation in the air." If the animals had an infection like hoose only those infected would be coughing, he explained, and they would cough twenty-four hours a day.

When he went home that evening at about seven o'clock, "I went to the bathroom to look at my face, and my face was burnt red. I was like a fellow made up for a concert."

Clancy was a crucial witness. He had arrived at the farm in the last days of 1981, but almost two years were to pass before he became convinced that the Merck factory was at the root of the trouble. He gave clear, precise and comprehensive evidence both of a practical and theoretical nature, covering the full range of conditions observed on the farm. He ruled out lungworm, the hoose parasite, through his own experience and close observation of the clinical symptoms. He had seen no cases of hoose since arriving on the farm.

Clancy described a further experience with irritation at the annual herd test the following year, in October 1984, on the kind of morning that country people describe as "a fine soft day." It was mild, calm and overcast and a heavy mist was falling when he arrived at the farm; what little wind there was came from the south-west As he pulled on his oilskins he felt an irritation in his throat and down into his chest. Again the animals were coughing. "The coughing this time was worse than I ever experienced it before . . . That morning after about an hour out in this mist the water started to drip off the end of my rainproof . . . My rainproof was dripping here onto the back of my hand, and I very soon noticed how stinging it was. It was painfully burning my hand. It was like as if someone was sticking a needle into my hand."

By mid-morning again the irritation eased off, and at the same time the cows stopped coughing. When he got to the younger animals at three o'clock in the afternoon there was no coughing, although the lungworm that causes hoose strikes mainly young animals.

Following reports of copper deficiency, Clancy had given long-acting copper injections to all Hanrahan's cows early in 1982, but it made no difference. In any case a survey of blood copper levels in clinically normal herds in the area revealed figures as low as a quarter of the level in Hanrahan's herd; in one high-yielding dairy herd the levels reported were so low that Clancy thought the laboratory had made a mistake. His conclusion was that there was very little relationship between animal health and blood copper levels. He quoted research undertaken in Co Kerry by Dr David Pool of An Foras Talúntais that confirmed his view.

Clancy had seen no brucellosis since arriving on the farm, and all tests were negative. Neither had he seen the clinical signs that would enable him to diagnose infectious bovine rhinitis (IBR), mucosal disease or leptospirosis as the source of the problems. He agreed on cross-examination that running eyes and noses, cough and vaginal discharges would indicate the possibility of those diseases, but they did not have the complete characteristics of any of them.

"You also said that clinical examination of the cattle showed no signs of any of those diseases," Peter Shanley asked him.

"That's right. I was satisfied that after a long year's work there that I wasn't dealing with IBR. I didn't go in the first day and say, 'This is not IBR' or 'This is IBR.' That would be a rash decision."

Commenting on the finding of antibodies for IBR and leptospirosis in blood samples by Dr James Neufeld of the University of Manitoba, Clancy said it merely indicated that the animal had been exposed to the germs. In the same way, after coming in contact with a flu victim somebody may develop antibodies for flu but no symptoms.

Eleven vets, including Clancy, gave evidence in the High Court. Two of them—Fitzgerald and Dodd—expressed no opinion one way or the other whether the operations of the Merck factory had any bearing on the events on the farm. Included in Brendan Walsh's veterinary practice were several farmers in the Ballydine area, some of whom he said were worried about the factory; but as far as he himself was concerned the problems in the area were no different from those he had encountered elsewhere. He did not think any of the sick animals he attended in Ballydine had ailments he would attribute to irritants in the air. However, he admitted that he would not know what to look for in animals affected by solvents or acids.

Walsh's partner, Martin Fitzgerald, expressed a similar view about the incidence of abnormalities in Ballydine. But he did admit to having a suspicion that something in the atmosphere may have caused sore mouths in two animals he had treated on Tommy Rockett's farm.

The county council vet, Peter Dougan, made four visits to the farm and reported widespread respiratory distress, lack of thrift, running eyes, and sore udders. "I thought it was a very, very well-run farm. There was three or four acres under galvanised [sheds]. It was spotlessly kept. There was some lovely calf boxes and grand calf pens." The respiratory distress was not due to lungworms, the running eyes were not due to pink-eye, and the sore udders were not due to cow-pox.

"Did you report back to the county council?" Tom Smyth asked.

"I did."

"Did you express any opinion?"

"I made up my mind that there was something wrong but I hadn't an idea what it was. They said it was being looked into and to leave it to them, which I did."

Dr Neufeld and the four vets of de Lacy's practice all identified emissions from the factory as the source of the animal health problems. Tom de Lacy, who had been visiting the farm for nearly forty years, testified that the management had always been good and that the family would follow his advice without question. But he began to notice the animal health deteriorating from the late seventies onwards, reaching a peak in 1981. He attended the farm over three hundred times in 1981, sometimes twice a day. He listed the symptoms as widespread coughing, pneumonia, tracheitis, bronchitis, pleurisy, eyes running, cataracts, noses running, dead calves and deformities, unusual incidence of twins, cows showing heat while in calf, vaginal discharge, early signs of labour in pregnant cows, loss of libido in bulls, stampeding, internal bleeding, blood in the urine, animals vomiting the cud, skin conditions, sore udders, and loss of milk yield.

"In regard to these symptoms which you observed, did you give the animals any treatment for these various complaints?"

"They got symptomatic treatment. The cows you couldn't treat, not a whole herd; and then, you see, the cows—the symptoms passed off during the day, the symptoms of the running eyes and nose, they passed off. There was nothing you could do there. The rest of the thing that was treatable, we treated it symptomatically."

"Had you any, had you any experience in your career like this, the number of animals with these varieties of symptoms in one farm?"

"Never, nor since either."

In the course of acrimonious exchanges with Merck's senior counsel, Kevin Liston, de Lacy rejected the notion that hoose was a problem in the herd or that the treatment he recommended was deficient. There were similar exchanges on the issue of brucellosis, a disease that causes abortion in cows. Liston put it to him that the birth defects reported were due to brucellosis; after all, thirty-six positive cases were reported on the farm in 1979 and were sent to the meat factory for slaughter.

"If there is any record anywhere—I don't remember the exact number—thirty-six cows had to be put down with brucellosis. Do you agree?"

"No, I don't. I will explain that to you."

"First of all—you can explain in a moment—you don't know?"

"I do know, and I can explain it to you. The animals failed the test. That doesn't mean—"

Liston wanted to move on.

"The witness is trying to add something," Mr Justice Keane intervened.

"Yes?" Liston conceded.

"The animals are tested for brucellosis. The animals that fail the test go down. It doesn't mean they have brucellosis. A lot of animals free of brucellosis go down in the test— not a lot, but some animals that fail the test are sent to the factory, irrespective of whether they have brucellosis or not."

There were no clinical symptoms on the farm, no abortions. In cases of deformity the pregnancies ran full term.

Martin O'Gorman answered most of Hanrahan's night calls for the de Lacy practice, because he lived nearby. He attended many births. From 1979 onwards he had noticed a serious deterioration in the health of the herd and described an increasing number of small, weak calves being born, drowsy and unable to suckle the mother. A large number of calves were small at birth. Some of these were deformed, with abnormal joints and curvature of the spine. There were also some freak calves born in the spring of 1981, and some born blind.

Earlier O'Gorman had described how he had been attending the farm since 1970, and he believed the management and nutrition were excellent. Lung problems began to appear in the late seventies. "The usual, the distinctive symptoms I saw at that time were mainly respiratory symptoms. I remember one morning seeing the whole herd, the cow herd, coughing, discharge from the eyes, running noses, and generally an agitated state. That was after coming in from the field for milking . . . I found all the animals that were sick after that, that this would be a constant finding, the degree of lung damage that I found with the stethoscope." He did not think the problem was lungworm.

"Have you experienced cows, or animals, cattle suffering from lungworm in the area?" Liston asked.

"I have never experienced cows suffering from lungworm."

"Never experienced it at all?"

"No," O'Gorman said flatly.

"Your practice has all been in the Suir valley?"

"It has."

"You have never observed it at all?" Liston persisted.

"I have never observed cows suffering from lungworm," O'Gorman repeated.

"Are you sure of that?"

"Yes, I am sure."

"Is lungworm very rare?"

"No, lungworm is a seasonal occurrence," O'Gorman explained. "Lungworm infestations; it tends to affect young animals in the fall, and generally where there is good management it wouldn't affect them."

Like de Lacy, he had seen no clinical signs of brucellosis at any time. Later Kevin Liston suggested that Hanrahan's purchase records for Multimast, a mastitis treatment, indicated that mastitis was a problem on the farm. O'Gorman explained that Multimast was used as "dry cow therapy." It was injected into the cows' udders as a protection against mastitis infection while the animals were dry. But he had also prescribed Multimast as a treatment for sore udders when the whole herd became affected with the condition in 1981.

Eddie Keating joined the de Lacy practice in August 1978. The symptoms he had encountered on the farm were mainly respiratory, but he also listed discharge from the eyes and nose, hair loss, vomiting the cud, sore udders, overgrown hooves, and calf deformities. In 1981 the animals had become "dull in themselves," especially animals in poor condition.

Like the other vets in the practice, Keating became involved in protracted exchanges with Kevin Liston about the causes of the various symptoms displayed, especially the poor condition of the animals.

"Did the lack of thrift—would that be related to the feed they got?"

"If animals don't feed properly, they weren't going to thrive properly; but from our observation of the feed on the farm there was nothing wrong with the feed on the farm."

"Generally we associate lack of thrift with lack of proper feed?"

"You can also associate it with other conditions."

"Generally we would associate lack of thrift with lack of good feeding?

"It can happen. It happens all over the place."

"It's a very simple question, as one professional man to another: generally would you associate lack of thrift with lack of good feeding?"

"Lack of good feeding causes lack of thrift. Anybody will tell you that. If you don't eat you're not going to—you'll fade away."

"Mr Keating, you are a professional man. You understand the question?"

"I do."

"You understand the question. Generally would you associate lack of thrift with lack of good feed?"

"If you have a situation where the feed—you have poor feeding, you will have lack of thrift in animals on the farm."

"I won't ask the question again."

"I've answered your question."

They debated again the difference between a reaction to the brucellosis test and the clinical manifestation of the disease, abortion. Keating insisted that there was no brucellosis on the farm. Neither did he diagnose IBR, mucosal disease, or leptospirosis. There were widespread weeping eyes and running noses, which would typically have disappeared by the afternoon.

"Would you do anything about it?"

"It depends on the form of the running nose he has."

"What form of runny nose would you do something about or what form of runny nose would clear up?"

"A lot of them will clear up. If I was to treat every cow with a runny nose I'd be a millionaire."

Dr Kevin Dodd, a senior lecturer in the Department of Farm Animal Clinical Studies at UCD, spent two hours on the Hanrahan farm at the request of Merck in February 1985, a few days before the case began. He described a well-laid-out and well-run dairy farm and a herd that he regarded as normal, well fed, and healthy. On visual inspection he found no evidence of coughing, respiratory distress, irritation, discharge from eyes or noses, sore udders, deformities, or skin problems. He saw no difference between Hanrahan's herd and that of his neighbour Pat Walsh, who had a dairy herd of comparable size.

"In so far as the animals you saw were concerned," Tom Smyth asked him in cross-examination four months later, "did you know in fact since then half-a-dozen of those animals have died?"

"I did not," Dodd responded, somewhat taken aback.

Pat Crowe was senior veterinary officer in charge of the Department of Agriculture's Regional Veterinary Laboratory in Kilkenny, where his main function was providing a research and disease investigation service to vets in practice. Following an approach from Hanrahan, he made his first visit to Ballycurkeen on 10 February 1981. He expressed no direct opinion whether the animal health conditions were related to the Merck factory, but he clearly regarded as significant the five cases of lungworm or parasitic pneumonia he had diagnosed in animals from Hanrahan's herd in the autumn of 1981.

"In relation to this," Peter Shanley prompted, "could you say anything about the condition of the herd having regard to those findings at that time?"

"With regard to that group of animals, or that age group of animals, one could comment that there was a problem with parasitic pneumonia."

"Is it possible for you to do this analysis in the regional veterinary laboratory, to describe the extent of the problem from the autopsies you did?"

"Back on the farm—yes, you would want to have seen the herd or the group of animals or the clinical situation."

"In relation to the findings of parasitic pneumonia among these five weanlings, is it possible to draw any conclusion about the prevalence of hoose in the herd?"

"Clearly they were heavily infested, those particular animals we saw—that I saw—did denote a heavy infestation of hoose." It may be assumed from this that Crowe believed hoose and not factory emissions to be the main cause of the problem. He went on to describe how adult animals pick up lungworms left on pasture by younger infected stock.

"What are the symptoms of reinfection hoose," Shanley asked, "as you might see them in the adult cattle?"

"Obviously, being a lung lesion there is an impairment of respiration and there is a certain level of bronchitis, and if it gets more extreme, either picking it up more locally or over a longer period, they develop coughs, which is the ultimate clinical manifestation."

"In circumstances where there is an outbreak of hoose among the weanlings in a particular herd, can one make any inference as to the likelihood or probability of reinfection hoose in the cows of that herd?"

"There is the likelihood."

On a visit to the farm in the autumn of 1981 he remarked to Tom de Lacy that severe coughing in a group of animals at pasture reminded him of hoose. De Lacy told him it could not be hoose, as the animals were regularly dosed, and he accepted that explanation.

The remaining two vets who gave evidence were career pathologists and academics, Dr James Neufeld of the University of Manitoba and Professor Hugh Pirie of Glasgow University. Most of their testimony related to the findings of autopsies, especially what was referred to as the joint sampling.

Three days from the end of the case Tom de Lacy was recalled to the witness box to explain the circumstances surrounding the arrangements for joint sampling of a group of animals on 15 September 1983. He outlined to the judge how relations with the Department of Agriculture had deteriorated. "The department weren't co-operating at that time, because we refused to give them the results of the toxicological examinations that we had already carried out on the animals." De Lacy was referring mainly to tests done by Dr Neufeld after 1982. "That was the only thing we had refused to give them, but we had told them time and again that they could come and bring any investigation team they liked and we would facilitate them in every way, except in that way. They wouldn't get that information."

De Lacy and Hanrahan had been asking for toxicological investigation, and the department offered to buy a number of animals, perhaps to monitor their progress away from the Ballydine environment, then have them slaughtered and sampled in the Kilkenny laboratory. But de Lacy and Hanrahan would not agree to the animals being removed to Kilkenny, because, although de Lacy himself would be welcome, the department would not allow Dr Dowding or Dr Buck to attend to take samples on Hanrahan's behalf. In addition, since Merck had also offered to buy some of his animals for post-mortem examination, the department's offer simply reinforced Hanrahan's suspicion of collusion between the department and his adversary.

Distrusting the department, they wanted a joint sample of everything, and in any case they believed Kilkenny did not have the facilities to do the tests. Their view of the laboratory's shortcomings was supported by the evidence of Pat Crowe in cross-examination.

"You have no expertise in toxicology?" Gleeson suggested.

"I wouldn't have expertise in toxicology," Crowe agreed.

"Did you have any facilities in Kilkenny for investigation of that type of character?"

"It depends on what you mean by type of character. We did do certain routine-type toxicological analysis."

"Industrial chemical poison?"

"We wouldn't have had experience of doing it."

"Would you have the facilities of doing it?"

"We wouldn't have in Kilkenny."

"Would you retain in Kilkenny, in your office, any books on toxicology relating to industrial chemicals?"

"Nothing specifically related to industrial chemistry. We would have some books relating to toxicology."

"Have you ever seen an animal, either alive or dead, suffering from the results of chemical solvents?"

"No," Crowe said, "I can't say I have."

☐

It was just after 10.00 a.m. on Thursday 15 September 1983 when Dr Mark Lynch got out of his car in the Ballycurkeen farmyard. It was a bright autumn day with a light breeze from the west, and more than a dozen people were assembled already. He noticed that his colleagues Pat Crowe and Philip Jones from Kilkenny had already arrived and were getting into their working attire. A group that included the Hanrahans, Tom de Lacy, Geoffrey Buck and Paul Dowding were surveying some animals in an open shed. Others he did not recognise, including two people setting up a video camera in a corner of the yard. The tension was palpable.

Lynch and a department colleague who had travelled with him had begun to prepare themselves for work when they were challenged by Hanrahan. He asked Lynch who had sent him and who his companion was. His director had sent him, Lynch answered, and he gave his colleague's name. When Hanrahan asked him to show his credentials, Lynch showed an identification card, but his colleague was carrying none. The tension rose, but the moment passed, and the business proceeded.

The gathering also included Hanrahan's neighbours Tommy Rockett, John Callanan, John Widger, and Joe O'Connell. They had finally agreed that the animals would be slaughtered on the farm, and independent tissue samples taken for analysis by each team. The Hanrahan team had picked a group of seven cattle and one pig, all showing symptoms of illness and not chosen at random. Three of the animals were from neighbouring farms. By half past ten they were ready to proceed, and the group moved to a large open shed with a makeshift operating theatre. Philip Jones recorded their visual observations on each animal as Tom de Lacy and Pat Crowe approached to take blood samples. In the corner the video camera began to roll.

As Pat Crowe moved from one animal to the next Hanrahan got the impression he was using the same syringe to take all the blood samples, and offered him some spare syringes. He said Crowe refused the offer and began to wash the syringe between samples in tap water.

"I was taking two samples," Crowe explained, "and I washed my syringe between the first and the second."

"Didn't Mr Hanrahan offer you a syringe?"

"He offered me a syringe of a larger capacity."

"Is it tap water you were using to wash out?"

"We were using saline to wash out the syringe."

"Are you sure of that?"

"I am."

"Are you sure it wasn't tap water?" Smyth continued.

"It would be water with saline added to it."

If this was the atmosphere in the court it was no better in the farmyard on the day.

Hanrahan's first animal was a ten-year-old Friesian cow with breathing difficulty and flaking skin around the head. She was coughing intermittently, and there was evidence of weeping eyes. After the animal was killed the four vets moved in and began to open it up systematically, examining each organ visually as they came to it and recording its condition. There was no dispute about what they were seeing. After the visual inspection, both sides began to take samples of the main organs for further analysis. For Hanrahan, Geoffrey Buck and Paul Dowding took possession of the samples as de Lacy removed them from the animal.

If the teams were in broad agreement on the immediate post-mortem inspections, there was no such accord on the results of the further examinations. The joint samples taken by Dowding and Buck for Hanrahan were sent for opinions to two experts, Dr James Neufeld at the University of Manitoba, Canada, and Dr Thomas Mullany at the Animal

Health Laboratory at Michigan State University in the United States. Mullany's findings were not available in court. Neither consultant reached the same conclusion as the Department of Agriculture on the condition of the animals.

The department's findings were a serious disappointment to Hanrahan. All the animals chosen had shown signs of respiratory distress, but the department's team found reasons other than airborne irritants for the problems. Of the two adult cows sampled, the department's report said one had a heart problem and the other had reinfection hoose. A four-year-old bullock had reinfection hoose also, as well as a piece of wire embedded in its stomach. A six-year-old bull had pulmonary actinobacillosis, a bacterial infection, and a calf had chronic bronchitis and pneumonia.

Hanrahan's experts, supplied with slides of the tissues, arrived at strikingly different diagnoses from the same material. Dr Mullany's overall conclusion was that the animals had varying degrees of interstitial lung disease and no evidence of infectious lung diseases caused by viruses, bacteria, or lungworms. He said toxins or their precursors were probably the most important cause of interstitial lung disease, an inflammation of the surfaces between lung components. Dr Neufeld came to similar conclusions.

"In relation to those slides," Tom Smyth asked Neufeld, "were you able to make any observation concerning what the slides revealed?"

"Examination of the slides—the main findings were found in the liver, enlarged nuclei in the liver cells and in the lung, where there was thickening of the alveolar walls—the small air spaces in the lung and in the spleen. There was a massive haemosiderosis, an accumulation of the blood breakdown products, the iron in the blood." This would indicate failure to recycle the iron by-product of red blood cell breakdown. Enlarged nuclei in the liver cells consisted mainly of cells with double centres.

"From such double nuclei in the liver cells," Smyth asked, "were you able to make any observation?"

"When we see lesions—we call them lesions—such as

this, we have to associate them back to what are the possible causes for these kind of things, and some of the things that cause this type of lesion are toxic chemicals."

Following his contact with the case in helping to analyse the slides from the joint sampling, Neufeld developed a continuing interest. His first visit to the farm was in late November 1984, when he spent four days examining the animals, studying the various reports, and discussing the problems with the Hanrahan team. He made another visit to the farm before giving evidence over two days in the High Court at the end of February the following year. By the time of his first visit the worst of Hanrahan's problems were over, yet he noticed some unusual symptoms.

His first observation on the herd was a general loss of hair, some animals having severe hair loss with thickening of the skin and flakiness or a kind of dandruff. "In examining some of the cows, just in walking amongst them and observing them during the day, you would notice some of them had a soft cough. It was not very pronounced, but it was what would be called a soft cough. I would say that there was a mild amount of eye discharge, but it was very minor. There was also a mild degree of nasal discharge, clear nasal discharge from both areas."

On his second visit he described the animals as being in fair condition, and walking among the cows he noticed that they did not appear to react to his presence as a stranger as he would have expected. He described them as "somnolent." This lethargic phenomenon both in animals and humans was referred to again and again by the Hanrahans, de Lacy, Clancy, and others, occurring especially at the height of the problem in 1981.

Neufeld had one cow killed for post-mortem examination during the November visit. His main finding was of firm or fibrous tissue in the liver. Returning to Canada after his first visit he brought with him for analysis a selection of tissue samples from the slaughtered cow, and blood samples from eleven other cows. As a result of this analysis he asked to have two more cows killed and further tissue

John Hanrahan (*Irish Times*)

The Hanrahan family in 1988. From left: younger son Ambrose, John, Selina, elder son Charles. In front, Mrs Mary Hanrahan.
(Jim O'Kelly, *Irish Independent*)

John and Selina Hanrahan in front of their house at Ballycurkeen, Co Tipperary (*Press 22*)

Aerial view of the Hanrahans' house and farm buildings

Pet dog on the Hanrahan farm (*Press 22*)

Cow with running nose

Deformed calves on the Hanrahan farm (*Press 22*)

Hanrahan farm animals being buried in mass grave

Peter Shanley SC, counsel for
Merck, Sharp and Dohme
(*Irish Times*)

Declan Buckley, General Manager,
Merck, Sharp and Dohme

Tom de Lacy, the Hanrahans' vet (*Press 22*)

Michael English, Chief Agricultural
Officer, South Tipperary

Tommy Rockett, the Hanrahans'
neighbour (*Sunday Press*)

Tom Menton of O'Keeffe and
Lynch, the Hanrahans' solicitor

Dermot Gleeson SC, counsel for
the Hanrahans (*Irish Times*)

JP O'Callaghan, County Engineer, South Tipperary (left) and Tom Rice,
Tipperary County Manager (*Derek Speirs*)

The Merck, Sharp and Dohme plant

slides sent to him. The spleens of all three animals had massive amounts of haemosiderin. "The accumulation of this haemosiderin in the spleen indicates that there must be some other occurrence or some other insults to the animals' circulating red blood cells," he told the court. "There may be destruction from things like toxic chemicals such as benzenes. In tests on rats benzene has been shown to cause this kind of lesion."

Like Mullany, Neufeld found interstitial fibrosis of the lungs. "The external surface of certain tissues of the animals can only react in a standard fashion to attacks of insults, and the lung in this case appears to be reacting to some kind of irritant or insult of some kind, and that is why there is the uniform interstitial fibrosis."

"What possible causes could that arise from?" Tom Smyth asked him.

"There are a number of possible causes, and one of them is inhaled irritants—gaseous-type irritants, inhaled particulate matter."

Analysis of blood samples from the animals revealed low copper and zinc levels. He also found antibodies suggesting that they had been challenged by IBR, mucosal disease, and leptospirosis, and there was a high count of eosinophil cells. These are inflammatory cells that may circulate in the blood as a reaction to challenges from parasites like lungworm, and they can also congregate in tissues after a parasite attack.

Under cross-examination Neufeld agreed that the low copper and zinc levels could account for some of the skin problems and lack of thrift; the high eosinophil count could be due to lungworm; IBR is a viral infection that could cause running eyes and noses and a soft cough; mucosal disease causes abortion and lack of thrift; and leptospirosis is a bacterial infection that can cause abortion, anaemia, red-water, and discoloration.

The trouble was that those explanations were too simple. It was a question of degree. Neufeld was not disputing the findings of his blood sample analysis, but argued that they were not sufficient to explain what was happening. Blood tests on most herds would show up antibodies of various diseases and low levels of copper or zinc without the kind of repercussions suffered by Hanrahan's herd. Eosinophils may simply indicate that the animal was subjected to challenge by lungworms; if it had succumbed he would expect to find parts of the parasites also. Copper and zinc levels were on the low side of normal but not low enough to cause hair loss.

Neufeld agreed with Peter Shanley that haemosiderin deposits can result to some degree from copper deficiency, leptospirosis, and red-water disease, caused by a tiny organism called *Babesia*.

"If the copper deficiency and the *Babesia* divergence are there, and if you were to add in another possible illness, the bacterial infection of the *Leptospira,* that again would have the effect of making the haemosiderin levels excessive?"

"If you had all those conditions together in one animal you probably would have a dead animal."

Shanley recited a list of the symptoms, again followed by Neufeld's blood and tissue analyses. "I have to suggest to you as a diagnostician as you are, that armed with those findings you would have to conclude that the changes you observed in the bloods and tissues are most likely to be caused by infection and from parasitic attack. Would you accept that?"

"No, I wouldn't."

"I have to suggest to you that all the evidence points in that direction?"

"In my opinion it does not."

Neufeld related the physical symptoms apparent in Hanrahan's cattle to the condition of the internal organs and body systems as he found them on post-mortem examination. Hair loss, skin problems, lethargy and even lack of thrift were associated with the functioning of the thyroid gland, and in the laboratory he found evidence of low thyroid activity. The obvious explanation was a simple iodine deficiency, but he did not accept this as the cause, as the animals had access to mineral licks containing iodine. More likely it meant the cows were being subjected to some kind of thyroid suppressants. He described these as chemical combinations based on the benzene ring. They could be in the food or in the air.

Turning to the skin surface damage, the thickening and scruffiness, he said that in the absence of lice or such skin parasites the commonest cause of irritation was ingestion of compounds like bromines, polychlorinated biphenyls (PCBs), or dioxins.

"Having made these various examinations," Tom Smyth asked finally, "did you form any view or any conclusion as a result of your various analyses?"

"It is my opinion that there is a high probability that some foreign substance or chemical, or a number of foreign substances or chemicals, are reaching these cattle and are affecting their metabolism and their nutrient function, because they don't appear to be completely normal in their general appearance, and I think—I believe the lesions in the tissues represent some form of insult to these animals that is not normal . . . I believe, and it is stated in some of the scientific literature, that animals can be monitors of what is happening in the environment; and after reviewing the cattle carefully and trying to determine if there was abnormality clinically, I believe that there is something affecting their general thrift."

However, despite Dr Neufeld's opinion his evidence was by no means conclusive. There were so many possible reasons for each condition that he was unable to say beyond doubt that any of the problems were due to toxic insult. No matter how convincingly Hanrahan's witnesses advanced arguments for chemical poisoning, alternative explanations were found by the defence.

Merck's principal veterinary witness was Hugh Pirie, professor of veterinary pathology at Glasgow University and scientific editor of the journal *Research in Veterinary Science*. A high-powered witness, he nevertheless had no experience of general practice. He did not visit the farm, and he made his assessment from a study of documents, reports and selected trial transcripts supplied by the Merck team. He had not heard the Hanrahan evidence or the medical evidence, or even studied the tissue slides.

"From the evidence you have read," Peter Shanley asked him, "can you indicate what allegations are made in respect of these reported conditions?"

"I think one important allegation has been that a lot of problems resulted from ... their immune system being depressed in a general sense; and having looked at the material referred to and listened to evidence here, I don't think that allegation can be substantiated from the information available. In a general sense problems have been attributed to exposure to toxic chemicals. I don't think that there is any satisfactory toxic data to support the idea that they have been exposed to significant concentrations of chemicals ... Thirdly, the pathological data that is available is equivocal in some respects in relation to the chemical theories, and I think a lot of the problems described could be due to known diseases of cattle."

At the outset Pirie divided the problems on the farm into five categories on the basis of the symptoms reported: respiratory distress, poor growth, eyes and noses running, reproductive disorders, and skin problems.

Shanley then directed him to the overriding condition, respiratory distress. From an examination of the various reports Pirie built a picture of a herd seriously afflicted by parasitic lung disease. Outdoors, he said, the young animals suffered from hoose, caused by lungworm. Indoors their problem was pneumonia, caused by other parasites. The adult animals in the herd were suffering from reinfection hoose developed as a knock-on effect from contact with the younger animals.

"If you were to put your opinion in percentage terms," Shanley asked, "could you express it in those terms?

"I think it is 99 per cent certain that the adult cattle would be exposed to lungworm and could develop pulmonary disease of various severities from that."

In cross-examination Dermot Gleeson referred him to diffuse fibrosing alveolitis (DFA), the condition diagnosed in two of the cows sent to the veterinary college in 1981. Hanrahan's advisers had uncovered a piece of research conducted by Pirie himself in which he had caused DFA experimentally in bullocks by feeding them a certain chemical.

"Would you be surprised if other organics of similar configuration produced similar results?"

"No, I think it is recognised that this type of lesion can be produced by other chemicals." He went on to suggest that the DFA in Hanrahan's case was caused by the animals eating mouldy material, either in their feed or their bedding, a reason also suggested in the veterinary college report. In fact the cows had been at pasture before being dispatched to the college for examination; they would have been eating grass, not hay. But Pirie persisted in his diagnosis of hoose.

"You would expect a final-year student to make a good shot at identifying hoose?" Gleeson suggested.

"Yes."

"If it was present on this farm?"

"I think so."

"And four experienced veterinary graduates from UCD would hardly miss it?"

"I think it is a question of degree, that there obviously was severe hoose on the farm." He suggested that the vets did recognise the disease but applied the wrong treatment. The advice given to Hanrahan was to wait until the hoose appeared and then treat the afflicted animals. Pirie, like Crowe, thought this was a dangerous tactic, as there was a serious risk that the pastures would be badly infected with lungworm parasites before the coughing animal was noticed and removed. He would prefer to vaccinate the whole herd of young animals in advance, though this could be difficult and expensive.

Pursuing the issue, Gleeson pointed out that nobody was disputing the diagnosis of hoose in five of the animal autopsies from Kilkenny in 1981 and 1982, nor indeed the four cases of parasitic pneumonia. "Go away from that and tell me was there any other worm found in any animal at any stage?"

"In the September post-mortems there were fragments of one seen in lungs of one of the cows."

"The September 1983 joint sampling?"

"Yes, one cow was diagnosed as having reinfection hoose on the nodules. The other cow had nodules also." Pirie went on to say that an additional two of the five cattle slaughtered for that joint sampling may have had reinfection hoose also, based on the incidence of eosinophils reported from the blood tests. His diagnosis of reinfection hoose was based mainly on the clinical signs of coughing as reported and the finding of remnants of worms in two of the four animals.

"What about the phenomenon of the vet's irritation going away when the cows stopped coughing?" Gleeson asked him.

"The only thing I might comment is that Clancy hasn't described he was coughing himself."

"He describes the irritation in his throat going away when the cows stopped coughing."

"If the cows had lungworm they might be induced to cough, and Clancy might have had a viral bronchitis."

"And a viral bronchitis, would that go away simultaneously?"

"It would be unusual. The cows stir up dust, and we have the same [symptoms]."

"Do you seriously want to put forward to the court as an explanation of what Clancy recorded that the cows were coughing because of dust and Clancy because of viral bronchitis?"

"I put forward that the cows were coughing because they had, basically, parasitic bronchitis," Pirie responded, before finally agreeing that his diagnosis could not be fitted in with Clancy's experience. They could not both be right.

Pirie went on to consider the serious loss of condition

in the herd, pointing out that the animals' reluctance to eat hay or silage must have been a contributory factor in 1981. Add parasitic infection, mucosal disease and the low copper status and there was no need to look further for an explanation. On the basis of the one positive result in April 1981, disputed in a parallel test, Pirie concluded that infectious bovine keratitis (IBK) or pink-eye could have spread to almost the whole herd and could explain the running eyes. Infectious bovine rhinitis (IBR) is a virus that can affect the upper respiratory tract and cause eye infections, nasal discharge, and coughing, among other problems. Pirie advanced a welter of reasons for reproductive disorders. The generally poor condition of the herd and the low levels of iodine in the locality would lead to infertility and would explain the weakness of the calves born; mucosal disease and toxins in silage could explain the deformities; and mucosal disease and leptospirosis could cause abortion, and antibodies for both of these were found by Neufeld in the blood tests. Brucellosis was another cause of abortion, Pirie pointed out, although annual tests had established that the herd had been clear since 1979.

Likewise Pirie's fifth category of ailments, the skin problems, were attributed to a variety of different diseases. The agent that causes cow-pox was identified in two samples taken on 30 April 1981. Pirie believed this could have been responsible for the sore udders that began to affect Hanrahan's cows in the spring of 1981. Copper, zinc and iodine deficiencies were well known to be associated with skin discoloration, dryness, and hair loss; and the all-embracing mucosal disease also produced a scab and dried scale on the skin.

Perhaps the commonest factor running through the autopsies was the repeated finding of fibrosis—thickening or hardening of the lungs, liver, and spleen. Eddie Keating, who did numerous post-mortem examinations on the Hanrahan farm, described the toughened livers and the absence of fat around the organs. Pat Crowe testified to finding fibrous livers in three animals in the joint sampling.

Indeed the Department of Agriculture report described the liver in one of the animals as being "very fibrous." Neufeld observed a very fibrous liver during the post-mortem examination he did on the farm. Pirie said fibrosis of the liver was associated with damage by parasites, pneumonia, heart failure, and chemical poisoning.

"Poisoning of one species or another would probably be the most common, be it from plants or chemicals?" Dermot Gleeson suggested.

"It is certainly recognised that poisoning from chemicals will produce toxic-level damage and fibrosis," Pirie agreed.

"That was found in some of the pathology [tests]?"

"I think fibrosis was found, from some of the descriptions. It was fairly localised, not necessarily generalised."

"Those animals undoubtedly had repeated attacks of something?"

"Yes, that's right."

"And something toxic, probably?"

"Possibly."

Samples of urine and kidney fat were also taken for testing from the animals killed in September 1983. They were analysed for eleven pesticides and other organic chemicals, because residues tend to accumulate in urine and kidney fat. The tests were done by Dr Mark Lynch at the Department of Agriculture laboratory, and showed negative.

"You tested for lindane," Gleeson put it to Lynch, "which is a contemporary insecticide, and for eight or nine obsolete insecticides?"

"Indeed the job of doing the test was—this was a routine test which would be done in our laboratory, and if an industrial contaminant [was present] that could have been seen on the chromatograph." Lynch explained that his pesticide unit had a particular expertise in the kind of organic compounds suspected of causing some of Hanrahan's problems: compounds containing chlorine. The routine screening they did for pesticides would have uncovered related compounds, which might have been the cause of the problem.

Gleeson suggested that it would have been more relevant to look for the list of chemicals used in the Merck factory and the list of organics that Jamieson had recorded in the Ballydine air. "Did you ever conduct any testing for any one of that long list of substances furnished to you by Dr Jamieson and Merck, Sharp and Dohme?"

"I'm not sure I understand your question."

"You have just been describing a total list, which would be derived from the list in court. Did you ever test or arrange for anyone else to test for any one of that very long, substantial list of substances?"

"No, we would have been precluded—were precluded from any such work, simply because we did not have the necessary access. We considered, in the case of the samples provided on September the fifteenth, doing some additional analysis above and beyond those that were in fact done. However, we were dealing with materials that in the main were volatile. Such an exercise was deemed as being pointless."

"This was September 1983. The problem had been going on for a number of years?"

"Yes indeed."

"It was still too early to test the dead animals for Merck, Sharp and Dohme chemicals in your view?"

"There was no point analysing samples for materials for which there was no evidence available to us to suggest that the animals were subjected to exposure which would lead to toxic impact."

A dioxin of low toxicity, octachlorodibenzodioxin, was found in a sample of Hanrahan's milk taken for analysis on 25 August 1983. It was detected at the Laboratory of the Government Chemist in London at 0.1 parts per billion. The same dioxin was found later in another sample from Ballypatrick, about four miles north-west of the factory. It came from the bulk milk of five farms in that area. The Lynch team reasoned that the most likely source of the dioxin was pentachlorophenol (PCP), a chemical widely used as a preservative on wooden fence posts and housing. So Lynch tested urine samples taken from four of Hanrahan's animals during the joint sampling. He found traces of PCP.

The next step was to establish whether PCP and dioxin were present in the wooden posts. Lynch got details from Avonmore Co-op of sundry purchases on Hanrahan's account. Among them was a quantity of fence posts he had bought in 1970, thirteen years before. Avonmore provided a sample of the same batch of posts, and it was found to contain low levels of both PCP and dioxin. A sample of milk from another farm ten miles away on which some fence posts from the same batch were used did not contain dioxin.

"It is likely that the trace content of octachloro dibenzo dioxin in the milk," Lynch concluded in his report, "resulted from exposure to the wood preservative pentachlorophenol, possibly resulting from contact with treated fence posts but more likely from contact with treated timber housing components (perhaps calf pens), feed packaging or storage bins, by a few animals in the herd." Hanrahan's pens were made of concrete and steel.

Kidney fat samples taken on 15 September were sent to the same laboratory in London to be tested for dioxin-related substances. They were found to have no residues of dioxins, furans, PCBs, or the closely related polybrominated biphenyls (PBBs).

The Lynch report's conclusion from the trace levels of dioxin found in Hanrahan's milk and the milk sample from the locality was that they had "no significance." While the dioxin detected was related to the dangerous tetra-chlorodibenzodioxin (TCDD), he pointed out that it is 50,000 times less toxic. However, there was little ground for complacency in view of the known toxicity of TCDD in even minute concentrations. And if one particular dioxin could be present, why not another, more lethal, kind? After all, no tests for dioxin were undertaken in 1981 at the height of the Hanrahans' problems.

In November 1987 Dr James Neufeld reported results of

testing carried out at the prestigious Mann Testing Laboratories, Toronto, for polychlorinated biphenyl (PCB), a highly toxic compound related to dioxin. He had sent samples of silage cut on the farm during both the summer of 1981 and the summer of 1984, and a sample of grain bin dust. The results showed that the silage sample from 1981 included 43 parts per billion (ppb) of PCBs. The 1984 silage had 174 ppb, and the grain bin dust had 730 ppb.

"The presence of PCBs in forage and dust from Ballycurkeen are strong evidence," Neufeld's report said, "that these compounds have been deposited on the farm property from an incinerator source. Atmospheric pollution of PCBs has been practically nil since 1975. Plants do not pick up PCBs when they grow, so they have to arrive on plant tissue by deposition from the air."

However, at no time was there any evidence that PCBs were either used or incinerated by Merck, Sharp and Dohme at Ballydine.

□

Only one of the eight vets who visited the Hanrahan farm did not describe a serious animal health problem. That was Kevin Dodd, who spent two hours there at Merck's request in February 1985, when most of the symptoms had cleared up. He said the herd was normal, well fed, and healthy. Among the catalogue of conditions observed by the other seven vets that they could account for in veterinary terms, the outstanding symptom was respiratory distress, which showed itself in widespread coughing and breathing difficulty. The remaining conditions were conveniently divided into poor growth, running eyes and noses, reproductive disorders, and skin problems.

Six of the vets who saw the animals said the respiratory distress was not caused by lung parasites. The seventh, Pat Crowe, indicated merely that their coughing reminded him of hoose. The four vets of Tom de Lacy's practice and Dr Neufeld were convinced that the problems on the farm were caused by toxic chemical emissions from the Ballydine factory. The county council vet, Peter Dougan, thought acid rain or some such irritant was responsible.

Heavy parasite infestation was diagnosed by Professor Pirie, who did not visit the farm. After a study of the veterinary reports he drew a conclusion that the young animals were seriously afflicted with hoose and parasitic pneumonia, and the adult animals with large-scale reinfection hoose. From the same study he attributed the non-respiratory symptoms to a variety of conditions.

The belief that the veterinary evidence would be able to establish the source of the animal health problems was seriously undermined by the case. Eleven animals were killed for post-mortem examination, 26 other autopsies were undertaken in Kilkenny, 120 blood samples were examined, and numerous undocumented post-mortem examinations were done on the farm, yet no agreed cause of the trouble emerged.

However, a common thread linking the investigations was that contact with chemicals in the Merck, Sharp and Dohme emissions *could* have caused all the conditions. Even Professor Pirie did not entirely reject that as a possibility. The alternative was that as many as twenty animal health conditions, ranging from hoose and pink-eye to copper deficiency and cow-pox, struck the Hanrahan farm independently and all at the same time.

10

MEDICAL EVIDENCE

It was ten minutes after noon on Monday 11 June 1984 when the members of South Tipperary County Council filed into the council chamber in Clonmel. At the top table the seats were already occupied by the chairman and council officials. Behind and to their right the press table was full also. Milling around the bottom of the room were fifteen to twenty people, jostling in the small space between the councillors and the wall. Among them was the taut figure of John Hanrahan, edging the group along to take up standing positions at the sides, behind the councillors.

The new county manager, Séamus Hayes, was presenting the IIRS report on the Merck, Sharp and Dohme incinerator. Nobody was listening. The bemused members wanted to know about the guests; it was highly unusual—irregular, some councillors felt. Nobody could remember if the council ever sat before an audience. Was it in accordance with standing orders?

In the rule book the secretary found that council meetings were supposed to be public. It was decided the people could stay.

The county manager and county engineer had sent their reports to members, giving their assessment of the IIRS report. There would be no cover-up, the manager told the council. Everything possible was being done, and none of the investigations had produced any evidence of a direct link between the plant and the animal health problem at

Mr Hanrahan's farm. All the recommendations of previous studies were being implemented. The company was monitoring emissions and the council was doing spot checks. "The results so far indicate that the atmospheric emissions from the scrubber stack have been within the standards laid down in the planning permission at all times."

Jim O'Callaghan, the county engineer, told the council that enough money had been spent on studies and safety and it was time to cry halt. He went through his report on the IIRS test, showing that the incinerator was in perfect working order. Acid emissions from the stack at times exceeded the permitted levels fourfold, "but emissions of this order are most unlikely to give rise to concentrations in the ambient air such as are associated with adverse health effects." They were caused because bad mixing of the feed tank led to high levels of chloroform going to the fire. He had now recommended that a bigger mixing pump be fitted to correct it. Seven organic solvents were detected in the emission gases in small amounts, well within the limits. "The emissions at start-up and shut-down times can be attributed to the fact that the temperatures were not adequate for total combustion at these times." He would not have realised how close he was to the kernel of the problem.

A second IIRS test was to be undertaken on the incinerator, he continued. "It is considered most unlikely that dioxins should be present in solvent incinerator emissions at the Ballydine factory, but, because of their emotive nature and the use of chlorinated solvents including chlorobenzene, it is recommended that comprehensive testing for dioxins should be carried out during the investigation."

Nobody would know whether dioxins were in the emissions or not, as the second IIRS test, six months later, would be done at the correct burning temperature.

Hanrahan had been forced to stand silent with a dozen local farmers and hear several councillors say that only one person was having problems with the Merck factory. Why did they think the others were there? Why did they think the council had an audience for the first time ever? Yet nobody had even asked their opinion.

"It will have to be law now," Hanrahan said as they left the meeting."

As part of the final preparation for court the family had to undergo further medical examination. John Hanrahan was first referred to Professor Muiris Fitzgerald in March 1980, mainly for wheezing, coughing, and chest pain. He was found to have reduced lung function, indicating obstruction of the air flow of the lungs. It suggested respiratory irritation caused by something in the air. In August 1980 Fitzgerald admitted him to St Vincent's Hospital for a thorough examination. His heart, liver and kidney functions were found to be normal, but the breathing abnormality remained. Tests for a variety of lung conditions proved negative. He was not a smoker, had no background or family history of lung diseases such as asthma, and had not got brucellosis. With no alternative explanation, Fitzgerald concluded that airborne pollutants could be causing the problem, and he advised him to pursue the possibility further.

"There are many examples," he told the court, "where dusts, fumes, vapours and gases can cause precisely the kind of symptoms from which Mr Hanrahan suffered and cause precisely the breathing function abnormalities that were demonstrated." In addition, in August 1980 Hanrahan was found to have a reduced white blood cell count, which can be caused by some drugs and chemicals, and which again left external contact as a likely source of the trouble.

On 9 November 1982 Hanrahan was admitted to St Vincent's Private Clinic after waking with severe chest pain and weakness a few days before. In the two-and-a-half years since his first visit to hospital the wheezing had abated, but he suffered increasingly from fatigue, lack of energy and poor co-ordination when attempting even the most routine farm work. Fitzgerald had had a letter from Dr de Souza, the county medical officer, saying that excessive amounts of bromine had been found in the course of a biological study in the area (the TCD report). He decided that a specific set of tests was needed, and referred Hanrahan to the State Laboratory for blood and urine tests for bromine.

The results were startling. The blood test showed a bromine level four times the normal; the urine test showed 250 times the normal level. The tests were repeated two weeks later: this time the blood levels were down, but the urine level had only dropped to 170 times normal. Fitzgerald referred him to Dr Michael Hutchinson, consultant neurologist at St Vincent's. Hutchinson found an absence of normal reflexes, and, since bromine can cause damage to the nervous system, this reinforced the theory that Hanrahan was the victim of toxic insult from bromine.

This became the subject of one extraordinary suggestion from Merck's counsel, Peter Shanley. In his summing up at the end of the High Court hearing he said Hanrahan had spent two weeks in hospital in Dublin before the test, so that the bromine could not have come from the factory. Nor was he suggesting it came from the medicine. "What I do suggest is that John Hanrahan, from one source or another but not from Merck, Sharp and Dohme, took a quantity of bromine or bromide from somewhere such that he showed something of the order of a thousandfold increase in his bromine level in blood and urine. It is not a substance that stays long in the body." He pointed out that a number of days separated the tests, and on the second occasion the levels were almost down to normal. (He did not explain how a level of 170 times normal remained in Hanrahan's urine at the second test.)

Dermot Gleeson immediately rejected Shanley's allegation. "It is now being suggested that Mr Hanrahan engaged in some sort of fraudulent ingestion of chemicals for the purpose of deceiving a test. I find it hard to recollect a more serious example of unfairness to any witness that was never put to him."

In response to a question during cross-examination

Fitzgerald had said that nobody eats bromine deliberately, although occasionally there might be people crazy enough to do so. But he had warned Hanrahan in 1982 that attempting to show that his condition was due to toxic insult from the environment would threaten his sanity. "I said to him, 'Don't let this drive you mad.' And in my opinion it would be perfectly normal, and an individual, any individual here in the court, including myself, would have their sanity threatened by the possibility that one's farm, one's livelihood, one's own health, the health of one's family were at risk in the situation where it would be very difficult to prove that risk and where possibly even obstacles might be put in one's way.

"I formed the opinion that Mr Hanrahan was under a lot of stress and his symptoms of fatigue could have been contributed to by the really intense psychological stress I thought he was under; and on occasions, in the absence of objective findings, I had that opinion quite strongly. However, with the emergence of objective evidence of abnormal levels of chemicals in his blood, chemicals which can cause symptoms but not produce any objective visible abnormalities, I had to weigh up every time Mr Hanrahan came to me could these symptoms be related to his intoxication of some kind from chemicals or could they be stress phenomena."

In 1982 Hanrahan was showing unequivocal evidence of airway obstruction in the lungs, and abnormal levels of chemicals were found in his blood. There was well-documented medical evidence that his symptoms of breathlessness, wheezing and irritation of the eyes, nose and throat could have been caused by contact with fumes of chemicals like ammonia, chlorine, phosgene, hydrogen chloride, and sulphur dioxide. Such contact might also damage the nervous system, leading to an absence of reflexes, documented in 1982 and confirmed on behalf of Merck in December 1984 by Dr Luke Clancy, medical director of Peamount Chest Hospital and consultant physician of respiratory medicine at St James's Hospital.

That lack of response was the only symptom of damage detected by Dr Clancy; he could find no evidence of lung damage.

In February 1985 Dr Clancy did a series of allergy tests, which all showed that Hanrahan was not predisposed to asthma, hay fever, or other allergies. He also did further lung function tests, and again found no evidence of airway obstruction and found Hanrahan's lung capacity within normal limits, although at the lower end of the normal range.

The only difference between Fitzgerald and Clancy appeared to be one of emphasis. Fitzgerald was happy to report that Hanrahan had suffered no irreversible damage to any organs, and he thought the physical threat to his health might be removed if the environmental influence was removed. "Having said that, it is correct that chemicals that are inhaled or swallowed have the potential, in years to come, to produce a variety of delayed problems, ranging from leukaemia to problems with fertility and reproduction. There is a range of possibilities. One couldn't quantify that risk. It is known that there are chemicals that accumulate, that can cause cancers and leukaemia, but if those chemicals are identified, that would be a question to be considered in the future. There would be a possibility about future problems due to already ingested chemicals."

In the autumn of 1983 all the Hanrahan family had a series of blood tests in an effort to detect evidence of toxic damage. Dr Rory O'Moore, consultant chemical pathologist to the Federated Dublin Voluntary Hospitals and St James's, found that all the family except Mary were suffering from what he called mild hyperchloraemic acidosis, which is caused by a combination of high chlorine and low bicarbonate levels in the blood. In three of the family, including John, there was also slight evidence of liver damage. Samples from seven other unnamed people, not from Ballydine, were normal.

"What is the significance of these results?" Dermot Gleeson asked.

"They are fairly mild results in fact," O'Moore answered, "but they probably reflect transient changes which are taking place due to various metabolic processes. The body, if we change it in one direction, has a compensatory mechanism to move in another direction, and this seems to be something like that that is taking place."

"So what are the probable causes of that condition?"

"There are several causes—kidney damage, even slight renal damage, that frequently gives rise to this hyperchloraemic acidosis, and it's due to the failure of the kidney when it's under some form of insult, is the word we use. It's failure when the kidney is under strain. It's a failure to excrete acid. You become slightly acidic." O'Moore said that bromide intoxication was one possible interpretation of the results. It had been shown to cause kidney and liver damage, but there were other possibilities also. "There are other solvents that I think have been mentioned previously in other evidence," he continued: "chloroform and several of the other halogenated hydrocarbons."

In cross-examination O'Moore agreed that acidosis was very common and could also be caused by heavy exercise, alcohol, and other factors, and was not a serious condition in itself. "It's a very mild disturbance to me. It usually is a sign that something is happening. It's not the levels of the change which were in any way endangering the health; what caused them might or might not have been."

The Hanrahans' blood samples and the seven other samples were also tested by Professor Ian Temperley, consultant to the Federated Dublin Voluntary Hospitals and St James's and associate professor of haematology at TCD. He picked out five of the twelve samples that showed blood cell abnormalities on a number of occasions; all were from the Hanrahans. He said the results were consistent with solvent poisoning.

"Can you say anything generally," Gleeson asked him, "or is there any available information in relation to the effects of solvents on the blood?"

"Yes, there's quite a bit of information regarding the

effects of solvents on blood cells. First, the worst possible feature of it is that it can lead to leukaemia, and secondly, it can also produce aplastic anaemia, which means the suppression of the bone marrow cells. And then it can produce a number of more minor effects such as the white cell count, a lowering of the platelets count, an increase in the size of red cells, and in some cases anaemia. This anaemia may be due to marrow depression, or in some cases there may be haemolytic anaemia associated with benzene and other solvents." (Such symptoms had also been detected in cattle from the Ballydine area.)

Apart from chemical poisoning, Temperley agreed with both Gleeson and Liston that his findings were consistent with a lot of other conditions, such as virus infection, vitamin deficiency, measles, chicken-pox, and glandular fever. But he said if the victim suffered from those conditions there would be other symptoms as well.

They debated a number of possible causes for Selina's persistent macrocytosis (enlarged red blood cells). This is a condition associated with certain forms of anaemia, and Liston suggested that the excessive bleeding over a period of years could have led to chronic anaemia and thus in turn to the macrocytosis. Temperley said that if Selina had anaemia due to excessive bleeding it would be associated with low rather than high red blood cell size, and anyway she did not have anaemia, "because all her haemoglobin levels, the blood level associated with anaemia, was at all times above the upper limit of normal."

On 1 February 1985 Selina was examined on behalf of Merck by Dr Dermot McDonald, a gynaecologist with twenty-two years' experience at the National Maternity Hospital, Holles Street, Dublin. In court he said that although she appeared anxious and somewhat distressed mentally, he found her physically well. "I thought Mrs Hanrahan presented gynaecologically with one of the more common histories and more common symptoms that I would see in gynaecological practice, and that is the problem of excessive menstrual bleeding."

She had told him that Professor de Valera, who treated her in the Mater Hospital, had diagnosed a condition called endometriosis, which is a growth on the walls and surface of the womb. McDonald said it was a condition for which no specific cause was known, but the growth is rarely if ever cancerous. However, that possibility may have explained de Valera's apparent alarm before he did the first operation in 1982. De Valera performed a second such operation in 1984, suggesting that it was still a problem. Indeed it was hardly surprising that Selina should have been anxious. Between September 1976 and September 1984 she had been ten times in hospital, seen ten different doctors, had repeated uterine bleeding and a bleeding ulcer, and had two major operations. In the meantime her husband and family had been ill and they were forced to move house and get away from the oppressive Ballycurkeen atmosphere. But perhaps most worrying was the sickness and death of so many of their farm animals and pets with symptoms remarkably similar to their own.

Almost all the symptoms reported both in humans and in animals could have been caused by disease agents. Common colds, undetected allergies, virus infections, alcohol, heavy smoking, heavy exercise, anaemia, gynaecological problems, inherited weakness, psychological stress, imagination or misadventure would explain the family's problems. Lungworm, virus pneumonia, pink-eye, rhinitis, mucosal disease, copper, iodine or zinc deficiency, cow-pox, red-water, inbreeding, stress, poor management or other factors could have caused the animal conditions.

The health symptoms taken separately had, perhaps, commonplace explanations. But to believe that such a variety of conditions could have struck hitherto healthy humans and animals at the same time on the same farm required a high degree of credulity when the source of a common explanation lay only a mile away on the floor of the Suir valley. Suggesting that emissions from the Merck, Sharp and Dohme plant had no bearing on the problems on the Hanrahan farm was stretching the bounds of coincidence.

Whatever about animal health, in the circumstances it seems extraordinary that the family was not subjected to a co-ordinated medical investigation involving all the resources at the disposal of the state.

11

THE SMOKING GUN

Dermot Gleeson lifted his foot onto the wooden bench, rested his elbow on his knee, and began to clasp and unclasp his hands, intermittently cupping his chin and stroking an imaginary beard as he spoke.

"I want to ask you in general about 1981. In general was the incinerator in 1981 running at 800 degrees or not?"

"No. It ran above 800 degrees for only 52 hours for that year, out of 1,382."

It was the twelfth day of the High Court hearing and Dr Paul Dowding had been explaining the importance of a high burning temperature in order to destroy dangerous materials. According to the makers' instructions the temperature on Merck's incinerator gauge should read no less than 800 degrees Celsius.

Materials in an incinerator can be burned to destruction at suitably high temperatures, and if it is done correctly and completely only carbon dioxide and water vapour go out the stack. The Merck incinerator deals only with liquids, and the fuel for the fire is the chemical material itself. The feed is pumped into the fire chamber through a nozzle that breaks it into a fine spray. Air is taken in at the same time to support combustion.

The waste chemicals at Ballydine are stored in a 20,000-gallon underground tank until enough has accumulated to justify starting the incinerator. Typically it operated about three days a month. When fully operating it burned seven tonnes of waste chemicals a day, a huge output if it happens to include dangerous material.

Complete combustion is vitally important. At lower temperatures some unburnt or partially burnt chemicals go out the stack into the atmosphere, but more critically, the chemicals can combine to form more dangerous products, of an unknown and unquantifiable nature. The new products could include dioxins when ring compounds like toluene are burned in the same fire as chemicals such as chloroform that contain chlorine.

The fire chamber at Ballydine is approximately five feet long and leads into a vertical secondary chamber. Five feet up into the secondary chamber are probes that measure the temperature, which is displayed on a gauge. Where the temperature is actually measured is thus ten feet from the flame; if the gauge is reading 800 degrees the flame will be about 1,000, which is the minimum temperature needed for complete combustion.

Dowding had examined Merck's log sheets for the incinerator, on which the operator had recorded the running temperatures over the years. The records showed that for most of the early eighties it was running at well below 800 degrees; in 1981 the fifty-two hours at the correct temperature represented only 4 per cent of the running time. Nor was it slightly below the limit: for over half that year it was operating below 600 degrees, and for nearly a hundred hours at less than 300 degrees. During the last four months of 1981 and the first two months of 1982 the temperature never reached 700 degrees at any time.

Over the following six months the temperature reached the recommended 800 degrees for only 5 per cent of the running time. In the six months to February 1983 it reached the critical temperature for a quarter of the time. Even in 1984—when the incinerator operation was already attracting a lot of attention—the temperature was recorded at the correct level only two-thirds of the time.

Nobody knows what came out the incinerator stack

during most of that period, because no emission measurements were taken. At the end of 1982 the company was forced to begin recording emissions and make a report to the county council. Even though it was a condition of planning permission, there is no record of what happened for the first seven years, including 1981 and 1982, when the Hanrahans' problems were at their worst.

Dowding had done another analysis of Merck's records, showing what the emissions from the incinerator were likely to have been at low-temperature operation. In April 1984 the company installed new linings in the fire chamber, which needed to be cured by heating them slowly. So they ran the incinerator deliberately at low temperature and measured the emissions at the same time. Incredibly, the fuel used for this curing process was the same toxic waste that the machine was meant to destroy when operating properly.

On 12 April the temperature never rose above 620 degrees and was measured most of the time in the 300s and 400s. Organic emissions recorded for that day amounted to 147 kg. On the following day similar temperatures were recorded, and organic emissions for the day were 181 kg. On the next two days, when the lining had been cured, the temperatures recorded varied from 750 to 1,000 degrees. On 14 April organic emissions were only 0.6 kg and on the following day 2 kg.

"It suggests to me," Dowding summarised, "that the temperatures of between 300 and 400 and 620 for which that incinerator operated for most of the period, the twelfth and thirteenth of April, these temperatures were not sufficient to destroy some of the organic material that was being fed into the incinerator, and this material was emerging in vapour from the stack." He consulted his papers before listing the organics actually recorded: methanol, ethanol, tetrahydrofuran, ethyl acetate, hexane, heptane, toluene, and chloroform. "I inspected the records carefully in the period that organic emissions were monitored, and found that wherever the incinerator was running at or near the correct temperature, the organic emissions were low."

Dr David MacSweeney, Merck's head of technical services, accepted that Dowding's analysis of the April 1984 experiment was a good guide to what was likely to have happened in the years when the incinerator was burning at low temperatures. But he was not unduly alarmed by it. "I again considered the basic measure of efficiency is the amount of material in the emission divided by the amount of material you feed into the incinerator at a feed rate of six litres per minute, which is at the low end of the normal feed rate; and taking the measuring number, which I think is 181 kilos, averaging over a day it would give an efficiency of 98 per cent."

The rating used for incinerators in the United States is a figure called the destruction and removal efficiency, which is the percentage of the material destroyed in the operation. For dangerous chemicals like those used at Ballydine the required efficiency would be 99.99 per cent. MacSweeney regarded an efficiency of 98 per cent as satisfactory for the Merck incinerator.

In cross-examination Dermot Gleeson sought out the weakness in MacSweeney's argument. "Can I suggest to you that that is a figure which is wholly unacceptable to the standards that apply for incineration of toxic waste?"

"I can't accept the underlying premise. Our planning permission allows for 150 kilograms per day of aromatic ring solvent. That number is the highest measuring number we have. It is still not outside the planning permission licence and it certainly is even at the—"

"I don't want you to deal with the premise but rather with the question. I want to suggest to you that the standard document in relation to hazardous waste incineration would find 98 per cent destruction of solvent completely unacceptable."

"It depends on the solvent you are burning."

"Can I suggest to you that the relevant regulations in the United States would require what they call a destruction and removal efficiency—DRE—"

"Yes."

"—for all organic hazardous compounds of not less than 99.99 per cent. Do you agree with that?"

"I am not aware of the regulation."

A look of satisfaction settled on Dermot Gleeson's face as he turned to study his brief for the next point. Mac Sweeney was a tough and intelligent scientist with a doctorate in organic chemistry, two years' service in the IIRS and a year at the Merck parent plant. Apart from his own contribution as the company's principal scientific witness he would provide invaluable support and information for many of the experts who testified for the defendants; yet he was not aware of such a fundamental regulation for so dangerous a machine.

"Is it fair to say," Gleeson challenged him, "that neither you nor any of the other distinguished and qualified persons who work there can detail what goes on when that mixture is fired and heated at different temperatures? You cannot exactly say?"

"We cannot exactly say."

"You cannot exactly say what compounds are created?"

"We cannot exactly say what compounds are created."

The Merck team made determined but vain efforts to refute what Dowding had uncovered, what their own incinerator records were showing. They argued that even though the reading was low, the flame ten feet away could be hot enough to destroy the material. But the most extraordinary aspect of the affair is that nobody in the company appeared to have looked at the records the operator was keeping until the Hanrahan team asked for them in preparation for the case early in 1984. It was only then that David MacSweeney discovered that it was actually burning at below the design specification. Up to that point the operator was simply instructed to see that the temperature on the clock was at 800 degrees.

Merck's general manager, Declan Buckley, pointed out that if there was incomplete combustion it would show up as black smoke, and there was no such indication from the emissions. (In fact one of the neighbours complained about a black plume coming from the incinerator in May 1981.) But he had to agree that an ordinary car engine operated with incomplete combustion and that usually there was no black smoke from the exhaust pipe.

"I am not going to go over in detail the two or three-year records," Dermot Gleeson put it to Buckley. "Again it is perfectly clear for the great majority of the time it was well below that, and often less than one-third of the temperature. I want to know if the utilities supervisor or the operator ever reported that, and if so, to whom?"

"To my knowledge, I have never seen any indication that the utilities supervisor had ever reported that up the line in terms of written documents."

"Is there extant anywhere in the comprehensive record-keeping system of your company any report or analysis or memo that records the problem of low incinerator temperatures before Dr MacSweeney's analysis?"

"Not to my knowledge." He admitted it was a crucial part of plant operation to see that dangerous toxic by-products were fully destroyed by burning them at the correct temperature.

"May we take it that no person in the management above the level of services supervisor interested themselves in this matter until the start of the year 1984?"

"No, there were operational problems associated with the incinerator that people involved would be involved in."

As soon as the slightest suggestion of tautology entered a reply Gleeson had a habit of folding his arms, looking up at the ceiling, and continuing his line of questioning from that position. "If there are people in management who interested themselves in the incinerator and the temperatures before Dr MacSweeney did it in 1984, would you give us their names?"

"Interested in relation to the log sheets?"

"What do you think I am talking about?"

"Is it the log sheets or other operations of the incinerator—the mechanical?"

"You think I am talking about the mechanical? You know I am talking about the incinerator temperatures."

Buckley got the message. "Outside the supervisors nobody else would have looked at them."

"Until Dr MacSweeney went?"

"Yes." He explained that they decided to examine the incinerator in 1981 after allegations by Hanrahan that the plant was causing him problems. Although their system of measuring emissions did not get under way until December 1982, they had examined the possibility of such measurement in 1981.

"It was to be another three years before you went and looked at your record in relation to the incinerator temperatures?"

"Before we went back."

"I want to put it to you that that represents grossly incompetent management, not to have monitored these results?"

"No, we were satisfied the incinerator was operating in a satisfactory manner, wasn't causing a problem internally or externally."

The evidence was indicating otherwise. On 28 November 1983 the IIRS began the first of two tests on the Merck incinerator on behalf of South Tipperary County Council, carried out over three days by Dr Ken Macken and two of his colleagues. Their report concluded that the thermal efficiency was good and the machine was in good working order. The flame temperature was adequate to burn the chemical waste completely. The temperature of the flame was 1,070 degrees, while the temperature on the gauge was 835 degrees.

For the second part of the investigation the IIRS sampled emissions from the stack and analysed a number of samples from the feed tank. Hydrochloric acid levels in the emissions were variable, and on two occasions they were several times the planning limit of 460 micrograms per cubic metre (1,755 during start-up on the first day and 1,476 during normal running on the second day). The report found evidence that previous monitoring of acid emissions had under-estimated them severalfold. The team concluded that the variability of hydrochloric acid emissions was related to the contents of the holding tank.

For hydrochloric acid to be formed in the fire and emitted in the stack gases there must be chlorine in the tank in the first place. One of the main sources of chlorine at the plant is chloroform, and analysis of three samples from the tank showed that it contained as much as 2 per cent chloroform. The remainder of the tank contents were made up of methanol, ethanol, ethyl acetate, tetrahydro-furan, and toluene.

The team concluded that the high chloroform reading was due to inadequate mixing of the tank because the pump was too small. Chloroform, being heavy, tended to settle at the bottom of the tank, from where the suction pipe drew its feed. They recommended that a larger pump be installed.

Macken and his colleagues calculated that when a mixture containing 1 per cent chlorine is incinerated it would lead to 460 micrograms per cubic metre of hydrochloric acid in the emissions. So another of their recommendations was that the feed tank not be allowed to contain more than 1 per cent of organics like chloroform which contained chlorine.

However, the IIRS team were unable to detect any chloroform in the emissions. Neither could they find phosgene (a component of the notorious mustard gas used as a poison in the First World War), which is produced when chloroform comes in contact with sunlight: there were suggestions that this might have been partly responsible for the Hanrahans' problems. Tests of the emissions for bromide and sulphur were also negative, but small quantities of fluoride and phosphorus were detected.

The IIRS report was presented to the county council, and in due course Dr Jamieson wrote a report on its implications—his third report. He noted that acid emissions from the incinerator exceeded the planning limit at times. But he concluded that, in average weather conditions, emissions of products like chloroform and phosgene were unlikely to lead to concentrations in the air that would be a danger to health in view of his own earlier studies of the air quality in the area.

However, he did re-examine the results of his second study, with the focus now on the incinerator. The highest concentrations of acid vapours he had reported at Hanrahan's farm had been in June 1981, when the Merck incinerator was used more than at any other time. His re-examination now showed a strong correlation between these results and the operation of the incinerator. He was at pains to point out, however, that the acid levels he had measured were unlikely to cause adverse health effects. He reported also that Merck process records "purport to show that the solvents incinerated at the time may not have contained significant amounts of chlorinated substances."

Jamieson suggested that it was important that a further investigation of the incinerator emissions be carried out after a bigger mixing pump was fitted, to ensure that acid levels could be maintained within the allowed limit and that highly toxic agents like dioxin and phosgene were not being formed. During the next test he said the tank should contain between 0.5 and 1 per cent chloroform.

So the IIRS was invited to undertake further testing of the incinerator, which they carried out in December 1984. Four samples of stack emissions taken at the correct operating temperature were found to contain no dioxins and no phosgene. The average hydrochloric acid level over four samples was only 19 micrograms per cubic metre, compared with the planning limit of 460. The report concluded that this low level was consistent with the chloroform content of the feed tank. Indeed it could hardly have been otherwise, since the tank contained only 0.05 per cent chloroform, one-tenth of the amount recommended by Jamieson for the test and one-fortieth of the amount actually discovered in the tank in the first test. Macken had not been told of Jamieson's recommendation. However, before doing the test he had discussed with the county council the possibility of "spiking" the waste to raise the chloroform content, but Merck had rejected the idea.

"The solvent fuel was well mixed, with an average chloroform content of 0.05 per cent?" Gleeson asked Macken.

"Yes."

"That, I suggest to you, didn't bear any relationship to, for instance, the extremity of the limit that was being proposed of 1 per cent, less still 2 per cent?"

"That is correct."

As an indicator of what emissions there might have been when the feed tank contained those higher levels of chloroform, the test was useless. But there was a more serious defect: both IIRS tests were carried out at the correct operating temperature. Everybody agreed that the combustion temperature was an essential element in a toxic waste incinerator, and, as Dowding had found out, the Ballydine machine was operating far below the required temperature for much of a four-year period.

Tests for products of incomplete combustion like dioxin at the correct combustion temperature could be expected to lead only to negative findings, and they did. To this day it cannot be said with any certainty that dioxin was not emitted from the Merck incinerator during the four years of low-temperature operation. But the IIRS team did not know about the low burning temperatures. They had never been told.

"I want to suggest to you," Gleeson said, venting his outrage on Declan Buckley, "that to permit the IIRS to write the second report without telling them what you had discovered about the operation of the incinerator for four years was a complete failure in co-operation and amounted to an act of deception?"

"I would disagree. We supplied them with the information they had requested at all times, and we at no stage made any decision in relation to the low temperatures, that we would preclude them knowing about it. It did not arise as a query."

"Is it like a barrister on a bad day, they didn't ask the right questions?"

"I don't think so. Even if they had got the information I'm not sure what relevance it would be in relation to their investigation, in relation to the homogeneity of the tank."

"Are you seriously saying that you don't think they would have any interest in the lower temperatures?"

"What I am saying is that they were charged with investigating the homogeneity of the tank and measuring the stack gases from the incinerator."

"Did you know that this was following on, that the 1985 report was following on the broader investigation of the incinerator that had concluded in 1984, praising its operation at exactly the correct temperatures? Didn't you know they gave that report?"

"Yes."

"Didn't you know that report was invalidated by something you had found out?"

"The report isn't invalidated, in that the temperatures they measured—they were quite satisfied with the performance of the incinerator . . ." Buckley went on to say that in any case the company's own monitoring told them that most of the time the emissions were well within planning limits. That merely invited Gleeson to point out that no monitoring of incinerator emissions had been done until December 1982.

Low-temperature operation was the most serious incinerator fault uncovered during the case, but there were others. As well as an undersized mixing pump there was an oversized fuel flow meter, which the company considered unreliable. In addition the automatic indicator of tank level was said to be unreliable; instead, as a measure of flow rate, they were using a dip-stick in the fuel tank to determine how much lower the level was after each burning—a rather primitive device in such a sophisticated factory. It turned out also that an automatic temperature recorder fitted to the machine was disregarded by the company, again on the grounds that it was unreliable. It was showing short-term temperature fluctuations, an indication of trouble they should perhaps have heeded. They had ignored also the manufacturers' instructions that when starting the machine the temperature should be increased gradually until it reached 800 degrees on the gauge. A recommendation that different burning temperatures be used for different solvents was likewise ignored.

"I want to put it to you," Gleeson rounded on Mac Sweeney, "that there was no real supervision of the temperatures for four years?"

"I wouldn't accept that there was no supervision. I will accept that the temperature should have been raised during the period 1980 to 1981 and 1982."

"Wouldn't effective supervision have noticed what was going on?"

"Yes."

"Wasn't it inefficient?"

"It was inefficient to the extent that it should have been recognised that the temperatures were low, in the sense that they would lead to levels of emissions, though harmless, that could have been reduced and should have been reduced."

This was still not enough for Gleeson. "It operated, I suggest, at dangerous temperatures."

"I wouldn't accept that."

"I suggest that a large volume of half-burnt or unburnt solvents were put out into the air."

"I will not accept that."

"It wasn't monitored at all until some time in 1982."

"That is correct."

"The monitoring was found to be at least partly defective by the IIRS. They recommended it be changed, and it was changed."

"I will accept that the partly defective surveys should relate to the fact that the results were less accurate than they should have been, but still—"

"I want to suggest to you that all these elements add up to very serious mismanagement of a very serious facility."

"I wouldn't accept that."

Indications that the efficiency of the machine was at best 98 per cent during low-temperature operations meant that 2 per cent of the waste material was going out the stack unburnt or partially burnt. At a fuel consumption rate of 7 tonnes a day this meant approximately 140 kg of incompletely burnt chemicals escaping out the stack. In fact in the only real test of what happened at this level of operation, the measured emissions were 181 kg.

If so much of the chemicals were getting out unburnt, at least part of the time, it is important to know what was going into the fire. Enormous quantities of chemicals are stored and used in the plant, many of them volatile and highly toxic. They are stored in thirty large steel tanks in an underground "tank farm." Most of the materials are solvents, which form no part of the final products but act as carriers in which more active ingredients are dissolved. The main solvents used are toluene, chloroform, methanol, ethanol, tetrahydrofuran, acetone, acetonitrile, monochlorobenzene, methylene chloride, hexane, heptane, and butyl alcohol. Not all are equally toxic but in addition there are highly toxic non-solvents such as hydrochloric acid and sulphuric acid.

There is no doubt that contact with such materials could account for the complaints from the Ballydine neighbourhood. Acids and solvents in the air would explain the irritation and respiratory distress, and solvent vapours can cause serious damage to blood, liver, and kidneys. Even the final products of the manufacturing process could be suspect if ingested in an unregulated way.

Many solvents are volatile liquids, which means they evaporate at low temperatures. They are therefore easily inhaled and can get to all parts of the body through the lungs. For the same reason their impact can be widespread in the body, the main health hazard being their ability to dissolve body fat and the fatty tissues surrounding the central nervous system. Short-term exposure would cause irritation of the eyes, nose, and throat, headache, nausea, dizziness, and drowsiness. Long-term exposure would cause dermatitis and affect the lungs, liver, kidneys, brain, and blood. A common effect is damage to the central nervous system, causing numbness, imbalance, lack of reflexes, and eventual paralysis. Some solvents are known to cause cancer.

A lot of court time was spent trying to elicit what materials exactly were finding their way into the incinerator tank. The uncertainty arose mainly because of the difficulty in establishing what impurities were likely to be contained in the waste solvents or in the "pot-still bottoms," the residues left behind when reusable solvents are recovered through distillation. It was accepted that a large volume of toluene, a ring compound, was being sent for incineration; and in view of the lethal potential of such compounds if combined with chlorine, it became important to establish the extent to which this, or indeed elements related to chlorine, like fluorine and bromine, were going to the tank.

A rather confusing picture emerged in court of the amount of unidentified material finding its way to the incinerator tank. The first estimate came from Declan Buckley during cross-examination.

"The unidentified components," Dermot Gleeson probed—"what percentage would they be of the solution?"

"Extremely low."

"Like?"

"We would have to look at the record for the past year to see if there were any still bottoms put in there. I don't think that there was."

"Go back a couple of years."

"Again I don't have a mass balance for it, and I don't think it is possible. I think it could be about 5 per cent." Buckley later amended his estimate of unidentified material to 1 per cent. David MacSweeney testified that 99 per cent of the materials they sent to the incinerator feed tank were volatile organic solvents they no longer needed but which they could identify—compounds like toluene, methanol, ethanol, tetrahydrofuran and ethyl acetate, whose chemical structures are well known. Toluene and methanol are hazardous chemicals by common consent. The remaining 1 per cent consisted of the residues of distillation; Mac Sweeney claimed that they could identify 0.9 per cent of these also, leaving only 0.1 per cent of the total unknown. Indeed he argued that the chemical composition of this unknown 0.1 per cent had to be closely related to the rest of the material, which was known to them.

The trouble was that the plaintiffs had no way of verifying the composition of the materials going to the tank. Hanrahan's team was unable to force the company to disclose exactly what their chemical processes were, on the grounds that the information was commercially privileged. The best they could do was to submit a series of legal questions, known as interrogatories, in advance of the case.

The interrogatories asked whether the Ballydine processes followed formulas described in certain chemical journals. They were answered, not by Declan Buckley or David MacSweeney, both chemists, but by Merck's head of engineering, Frank Wyatt. In all cases the response was, "The Defendant does not know." During the hearing it emerged that the answers to the interrogatories were available at Ballydine in a company publication. Gleeson took up the issue with MacSweeney.

"Do you have something called the *Merck Index* on site?"

"Yes."

"What is that?"

"That is a journal that is put out by our company. It contains information on a vast number of pharmaceutical products."

"Can I show you its entry for indomethacin?" Gleeson pointed out the answer to one of Hanrahan's questions in the journal. "Do you see in the middle, *'Journal of the American Chemical Society*, 488'—the middle of the page? I fully appreciate that Mr Wyatt may have had assistance in answering these questions. Did you assist him?"

"Yes."

"Can I suggest to you that a similar response was made in respect of sulindac and amitriptyline, and again the *Merck Index* clearly discloses it?"

"We were advised by our solicitors that we were not under any obligation to search any literature to establish it if we didn't know the answer."

"You knew this was a case being brought by a farmer, who wouldn't know much about what went on in the plant?"

"Yes."

"The only way he could find out was by asking you questions?"

"Yes."

"Did you not think it would have been reasonable to look up the *Merck Index* to see whether it could help you?"

"Our advice from our solicitor was that we were not under any obligation to do that and we should not do any searching."

So having been forced to acquire the expertise that would enable them to ask the right questions, the plaintiffs found that the company was not obliged to answer them frankly, even when the information was readily available.

MacSweeney pointed out that Merck's raw materials were no more than combinations of seven elements—carbon, hydrogen, oxygen, nitrogen, sulphur, fluorine, and chlorine—and that their further combination would result in compounds containing the same elements. But he had to agree that there were hundreds of thousands of variations in the way these elements could be linked up, depending on the conditions under which they are brought together. Variants with slight differences in molecular structure would have very significant differences in toxicity. The highly toxic chemical involved in the Seveso disaster was 2,3,7,8-tetrachlorodibenzodioxin; another dioxin, about a thousand times less toxic, contains exactly the same elements, and the same number of atoms, the difference being in the arrangement of the atoms. So knowing the general nature of the processes would not necessarily make it possible to identify the by-products of their reactions.

Nevertheless the court was able to elicit a certain amount of information. It was David MacSweeney who explained that the 1 per cent of incinerator fuel arising from distillation residues must contain the by-products of the reactions in which the solvents participated before they were distilled. He quoted the example of ethanol, used in the manufacture of sulindac. "The residue that is left contains the known by-products of the sulindac process. These residues would contain sulindac itself and products related to sulindac. These would constitute the great majority, 90 to 95 per cent, of the residue which is sent occasionally to the incinerator feed tank."

In the same way toluene is one of the carrier solvents in the manufacture of indomethacin. "In 1978 we sent the still residues from the recovery of toluene in the indomethacin process to the waste tank for incineration. These residues would again contain principally the indomethacin, plus the known by-products . . . Indomethacin and the other by-products I have listed again are principally made up of carbon, hydrogen, and oxygen, with two additional elements, nitrogen and chlorine."

He produced the chemical formulas for sulindac and indomethacin, showing them to be a complicated series of ring structures containing carbon, hydrogen, oxygen, nitrogen, sulphur, fluorine, and chlorine. The intermediates were of the same general structure. So the residues from the recovery of ethanol and toluene would include fluorine and chlorine attached to ring compounds. Those residues were sent for incineration at least occasionally.

Documents produced in court indicated that chlorine was involved in the making of three other Merck products—amitriptyline hydrochloride, cyclobenzaprine hydrochloride, and cyproheptadine hydrochloride—and that solvents used in the manufacture of these products were sent to the incinerator after distillation. It is not unreasonable to conclude that they may have been contaminated with chlorine.

Monochlorobenzene, the solvent detected by Dr Jamieson simultaneously in the process stack emissions and at Hanrahan's farm, is one of the solvents used in the amitriptyline hydrochloride process. According to Merck it was not sent to the incinerator, but in fact it was found there at least once; company records made available to the court show that it accounted for over 1 per cent of the feed tank in a test sample on 1 December 1981. In any case monochlorobenzene could arise from the break-up of the ingredients already in the tank.

Part of the molecular structure of indomethacin is a protruding benzene ring with one chlorine atom attached. If this breaks off in incineration, David MacSweeney told the court, the product would be monochlorobenzene.

"Is monochlorobenzene a possible precursor of dioxin?" Dermot Gleeson asked him.

"There is a debate about that in the literature. It is possible."

They went on to discuss the possibility of similarly toxic products arising when sulindac was heated. In the end MacSweeney had to admit that, while he could reasonably say where molecules would break, the products of recombination were less easily predicted. Indeed Merck were unable to explain either how phosphorus was detected in the stack emissions by the IIRS or how sodium hydroxide and acetonitrile got into the tank on other occasions. According to the company's reasoning, none of these three products should have been there.

But it was in accounting for the destination of chloroform that the Merck explanations were least satisfactory. The company used an estimated 137 tonnes a year in the making of sulindac. Court documents showed that solvents recovered from this process were sent for incineration, and that they contained chloroform as an impurity at up to 0.5 per cent. The IIRS tests showed that in 1983 and 1984 the tank contained chloroform at up to 2 per cent, and there were indications that the proportion may have been twice that level.

But the question of whether chloroform was sent to the incinerator tank before 1982 led to a conflict of evidence between Declan Buckley and David MacSweeney.

"Have you consistently burned chloroform in this incinerator?" Gleeson directed the question at Buckley.

"Yes. The conditions were modified in 1976 for sulindac. That is why the limit was put on the HCl in 1976—the hydrochloric acid. It would be recognised that there would be trace amounts of chloroform in the sulindac waste streams."

It was an unequivocal statement, giving a reasoned explanation. But three days later Buckley's statement was partly contradicted by MacSweeney.

"One thing I want to clear up," Peter Shanley asked. "To what extent is there chlorinated product being fed to the incinerator?"

"Prior to December 1982 chlorinated solvent was not fed into the incinerator feed tank. After December 1982 low levels of chloroform in an impurity in stream for the solvents recovered from the low-volume stream were sent to the incinerator feed tank. The level of chloroform in the overall incinerator feed tank would not have exceeded 1 per cent."

"Do I understand from your answer that between and during 1976 to 1981 there was no chloroform in the incinerator?"

"Yes, that is correct, right up to the end of 1982." Up to that time the company had sold the chloroform to an outside buyer; but there was no attempt to explain how Buckley would have been unaware of this arrangement.

Neither Buckley nor MacSweeney seemed unduly alarmed that unburnt or partly burnt chloroform might have been getting out of the incinerator. MacSweeney agreed reluctantly that chloroform converts to phosgene in bright sunlight, but took refuge in debating concentration levels when asked to agree that either phosgene or chloroform might be dangerous.

Gleeson questioned him on the consequences of burning chloroform. "You could have complete combustion, in which case you would get hydrogen chloride?"

"Yes."

"Which is itself poisonous, highly toxic?"

"At a certain concentration."

"Yes, but relative to other substances it would be regarded as highly toxic?"

"Relative to a loaf of bread, yes, but other things, no."

"Do you think that is a full answer to my question?" Gleeson did not appreciate the witticism.

"I think all of these things are concentration-related."

They continued to disagree about the toxicity of hydrochloric acid.

"Is it more or less toxic than chloroform?"

"I don't know. I would have to check the record."

"I want to suggest to you that chloroform yields over 90 per cent of its weight in hydrochloric acid gas when it is burned."

"I would accept that."

"Do you think or not think that if you are going to burn chloroform there should be a concentration on the relationship—?"

"We don't burn chloroform. We burn chloroform as a low-level—as low-level impurities in the fuel we send to the incinerator. The level of impurities is of such a sufficiently low level that when it emits from the top of the stack it is harmless on dispersion."

"The level you gave for daily consumption in the incinerator was 7,000 litres?"

"Yes."

"Two per cent of that is 140 litres, and 1 per cent is 70 litres?"

"Yes."

"I want to suggest that 70 litres is a great deal of chloroform."

"It is not a great deal, depending on what context you are talking about. If you are talking about 70 litres of chloroform being dispersed over twenty-four hours from the stack of a building it is not a significant harmful factor to the environment or otherwise."

Once it got into the incinerator there were a number of possibilities for chloroform. It could go out the stack as unburnt chloroform (which might or might not become phosgene in the air); it could form hydrochloric acid emissions; or it could become available for attachment to ring compounds in forming dioxins, furans, or other such compounds. None of those possibilities allowed for complacency.

Under American regulations a scrubber must be fitted to incinerators expected to be emitting more than 4 pounds (1.8 kg) of hydrochloric acid an hour. Declan Buckley agreed that such a scrubbing device could be fitted for about £100,000. According to Dr Richard Magee of the New Jersey Institute of Technology, an expert on incineration of toxic waste, there is no doubt that an incinerator burning up to 2 per cent chloroform at 98 per cent efficiency would need a scrubber; apart from the real danger of dioxins and furans being produced as products of incomplete combustion, it would be emitting large quantities of unburnt chloroform, which causes cancer.

According to Dr MacSweeney, in 1981 chloroform could also have come through the scrubber stack on top of the process building. This stack takes the output from two scrubbers that are connected to about thirty huge reaction vessels throughout the building. The scrubbers neutralise toxic gases and vapours by spraying them with water or sodium hydroxide before releasing them to the air. The scrubber will be reasonably effective in stopping solvents that are water-soluble, such as methanol and ethanol, but not chloroform and toluene, which are non-soluble.

From 1982 onwards the records show that chloroform was one of the solvents detected in scrubber emissions, along with methanol, ethanol, acetonitrile, acetone, toluene, monochlorobenzene, and others. The planning permission allows small levels of acid and organic emission from the scrubber stack: 460 micrograms per cubic metre of hydrochloric acid, and 150 kg per day of organic material.

David MacSweeney said the levels of chloroform that got through would have been harmless; but since there was no regular measurements at the time, there is no way of knowing, as Dermot Gleeson was quick to point out.

"There are no measurements," MacSweeney agreed. "But it is quite possible to infer what they were, because the procedures which are used to control organic emissions— which are the use of condensers and tied into the scrubber system—have remained the same since 1976 to the current time, and the emissions record since 1982 onwards would be good information of what was emitted in the previous years, because the precise operation would not have significantly changed."

After monitoring began, the levels of chloroform emitted were regularly above 50 kg a day during the manufacture of sulindac, although well within the planning limit of 150 kg. MacSweeney pointed out that Jamieson's monitors did not pick up excessive levels of organics in either of his studies in 1980 or 1981. But some limited spot checking of the scrubber stack emissions had been done before 1982. They showed that planning limits had been breached.

On 6 November 1981 Byron Roe, general manager of Merck, Sharp and Dohme, wrote to Jim O'Callaghan, the county engineer: "During May and early June of 1980, the data indicates violation of the permit limits. This occurred during a period when one of the Amiloride steps was in operation and severe mechanical problems were experienced with the scrubber . . ." The details showed that hydrochloric acid emissions exceeded the planning limit on each of the five occasions when they were measured in 1980. The highest level recorded was 1,796 micrograms per cubic metre, four times the limit, and the lowest was two-and-a-half times the limit. Hydrochloric acid emissions had been measured in October 1979 and were measured again in October 1981; on both occasions they were well inside the limit, but the only five measurements taken in that two-year intervening period exceeded the limit severalfold.

Roe had enclosed with the letter all the emission test results carried out by Merck since the factory opened—sixteen tests for hydrochloric acid, ten for sulphur dioxide, and four for organics. No other monitoring had been carried out over the six-year period since 1976, so there is no way of knowing for certain what emissions there were.

Roe's letter arose as a result of Dr Jamieson's investigations for his second report, and the breaches might not have come to light otherwise. While examining the company's records Jamieson had discovered the results, and brought them to the company's attention. This resulted in the letter to O'Callaghan, who called a series of meetings with the company, and a more regular monitoring programme was agreed. But no other action was taken and the county council was not told of the breaches, although this was at the height of the Hanrahan controversy.

The county manager, Tom Rice, had told the council in November 1982: "The company has complied at all times with the terms and conditions laid down for its operation." In the light of these breaches of permit, this statement was less than accurate. Neither did Jim O'Callaghan include a reference to the breaches in his summary of the Jamieson report to the council, although they had been mentioned in that report.

The High Court record reveals a series of reports on accidents and abnormalities in the early nineteen-eighties. They show that the plant was having difficulty controlling unplanned emissions, especially during the manufacture of sulindac. Apart from the odour complaints due to thio-anisole, acid emissions appeared to be a problem. In February 1981 a number of emissions were noted, which led to an instruction to the production staff that no hydrochloric acid emissions should be tolerated under any circumstances. The procedure for venting the acid was revised, with a significant improvement; but there were many other releases.

In October 1979 a quantity of chlorine got out while

being fed through a pipe to the main building from an outlying storage point. A line to the scrubber had been left open, and when it became overloaded the chlorine vapour began to leak out through the stack. Nobody knows how much escaped, but 150 kg had to be replaced. Richard Ruch, the American meteorologist engaged by Merck to help them defend the action, estimated that if the worst conditions applied at the time of that release, 150 kg escaping from the scrubber stack could have led to a one-hour concentration of almost 5,000 micrograms per cubic metre at Hanrahan's farm. David MacSweeney said that only a small proportion of the gas escaped.

In July 1980 a mixture of alcohol and cyproheptadine hydrochloride, one of Merck's finished products, escaped through a vent. Quantities of indomethacin, another finished product, escaped on at least four occasions between January 1979 and September 1982.

Apart from the scrubber stack, there are numerous vents on the roof of the process building that allow for what are described as "fugitive emissions." Most of them lead from the reaction vessels, each of which is equipped with a safety valve that releases material if the pressure gets too high. Another pipe is open to the roof from each vessel when the process is water-based, when emissions are considered safe; and yet another pipe is used during washing operations. A series of vents provide roof exits for steam built up in the water jackets and from vacuum-based driers. And finally the air in the building is ventilated every five or six minutes through a network of air vents. Court documents show that, in all, the plant has 227 vessel vents on the process building, 29 in the solvent recovery unit, and 37 in the air movement system, a total of 293.

"In relation to the safety lines," Gleeson was questioning Buckley, "is there any record kept of how often they are open or closed?"

"There isn't a record kept. They are serviced every six months. It is extremely rare."

"We will come to the rarity of it. Is there any set of

sheets or paper that will tell you how often the safety lines in the vessels have lifted?"

"No, there isn't."

Gleeson turned to the vessel vents that are open to the atmosphere during water-based reactions. "Is there anywhere I could learn how often the reaction vessels were opened to the atmosphere?"

"I think the incident report would highlight most of them."

"If you wanted to find out how often it was happening, how would you go about finding out?"

"You would ask—it would depend on whether the production supervisor issued a report or not on one of these incident forms."

"If he did not?"

"Then he would not know about it."

"If he did not do that, put it into the incident form, it wouldn't be recorded?"

"Not necessarily, no."

□

Factory emissions became a source of discomfort in the Ballydine neighbourhood after the manufacture of sulindac began in 1978, but it was not until the Hanrahan case began to cause widespread disquiet that Merck undertook any serious monitoring. Up to the end of 1982 there were no more than occasional checks of the scrubber stack emissions and no monitoring at all of the incinerator. The spot checks indicated that the planning limits were exceeded significantly at least for hydrochloric acid in 1980.

But even after serious monitoring began in 1982 the breaches continued intermittently. Dr Paul Dowding presented an analysis of chloride emissions from the incinerator, which showed that of the thirty-four measurements carried out between December 1982 and June 1984 the planning limits were exceeded on five occasions. This did not include the two breaches reported by the IIRS, which the company monitoring did not appear to pick up; neither did it take into account that, as the IIRS reported, the monitoring technique being used was probably underestimating results.

No chemical plant can be expected to operate without emissions of one kind or another. Low levels are allowed by planning permission, levels that are believed to be within safe limits. Of the three sources of emission subject to planning permission at the Merck plant, two of them—the scrubber stack and the incinerator stack—exceeded those limits several times.

But nobody knows exactly what was happening for the first six years. There is still no measurement of what comes out intermittently as fugitive emissions from the many vents on the roof of the process building. Hydrochloric acid has escaped from the scrubber, the incinerator and other exit points in excessive amounts. Jamieson detected toluene in the scrubber and incinerator emissions, and monochlorobenzene from the scrubber stack. Merck witnesses have admitted that toluene, chloroform and other organics escaped through the scrubber when it became overloaded. Many other substances are known to have escaped, including at least two of the finished drugs made at the plant. It is possible that unknown materials, the result of chemical combination, escaped also.

What is known is that from the time the plant opened, the incinerator mixing pump was too small, the flow meter was too big, the automatic temperature recorder was unreliable, the toxic fuel gauge was unreliable, the makers' instructions were ignored, and nobody paid too much attention.

What is known is that for at least four of those years the incinerator was running erratically and the gauge was saying that the burning temperatures were often well below what would be required for complete combustion. In the tank at the time were a selection of organic and ring compounds, especially toluene, and a selection of chlorine compounds, especially chloroform. What is known is that such conditions lead to products of incomplete combustion that can include dioxins and furans, which are highly toxic in tiny amounts, as well as entirely unknown products.

Perhaps most remarkable of all is that none of the public and private investigators noticed that incinerator spluttering out unidentified chemicals through its fifty-foot stack. Here was the smoking gun.

12

THE MISSING LINK

"I want to come to what may well be the most important point in the case and is certainly the most important point in relation to emissions."

It was 4 July 1985, the last day of the High Court case, and Dermot Gleeson was coming to the end of his closing submission. "It relates to the question of daily averages, weekly averages, and checks." He paused before launching into a story about two neighbours having a bath at the same time. The court relaxed, happy that Gleeson was so quickly relieved of the burden of gravity.

The bathing was taking a long time; in fact they were all day in the bath. One man was enjoying himself in nice lukewarm water; but every few hours somebody came and poured boiling water over his neighbour. The temperature of the bath water was being taken at the same time, he explained; and at the end of twenty-four hours the average temperature of the baths was the same.

"It is possible that you would get scientists and doctors who had not seen the burns on the back of the man who had the boiling water come in on top of him to give evidence that his average daily temperature was lukewarm, and it was well established in every country in the world that lukewarm water did no harm to a human being, and that there was never reported damage to monkeys and rabbits that had been bathed in it for six hours at a time without any problem, and it was inconceivable that there was any damage. That is the key to this case . . ." The average level measured over twenty-four hours disguised the posssibility of short-term peaks.

☐

On Thursday 20 September 1979 Angus Graham, utilities superintendent at Ballydine, was returning from a visit to Hanrahan's farm. "On the way back to the plant the path of the boiler fumes was clearly visible, rising approximately 100 feet and inverting slowly back to ground level. It is probable that some of the grounds for Hanrahan's complaint is the boilerhouse emission, which would contain SO_2 [sulphur dioxide] or SO_3 [sulphuric anhydride] fumes, would smell sulphury and stink generally. His place is well situated, given the correct light wind direction, to catch the plume, especially on a hazy or foggy morning."

Graham did not give evidence in court, but his observations about the path of the boiler stack fumes were raised. They were dismissed by David MacSweeney as misinformed—on the grounds that Graham was not a meteorologist, and that if the boilerhouse plume regularly moved towards Hanrahan's farm, Dr Jamieson's measurements of air quality would have been much different.

Because of the court case, the eyewitness accounts that have attracted most attention are mainly those of the Hanrahan family, but the court record shows that there were 227 odour complaints to the factory, and only 34 came from the Hanrahans. Those who made the complaints were saying that something in the air was causing burning and irritation of eyes, nose, and throat, coughing, wheezing, chest pains, nausea, headache, and drowsiness. In cattle something in the air or on the grass was causing running eyes and noses, coughing, stampeding, erratic behaviour, sore udders, and unpalatable grass and silage. At a more serious but less clear-cut level in animals there were birth defects, reproductive disorders, wasting and blood abnormalities, lung, liver and kidney damage, and deaths.

The Merck factory was emitting the kind of substances that could give rise to these symptoms if they arrived in high enough concentrations. But measurements had shown that the concentrations arriving could not have caused the symptoms. There was a missing link.

The levels of chemicals like hydrochloric acid that are regarded as acceptable in the air vary widely from country to country, but the levels at which they can be detected by smell, irritation or respiratory distress are well established. It follows therefore that the eyewitnesses were mistaken, or that Dr Jamieson's equipment did not give an accurate picture, or that the symptoms reported were due to something other than chemicals in the air.

It is possible that the Hanrahan family exaggerated to some extent the impact the emissions were having on them; but it is inconceivable that they are entirely mistaken. It is fatuous to suggest that there could have been a conspiracy among neighbours, vets, scientists and even Merck witnesses to acquiesce in such a litany of complaints. The inescapable conclusion is that the eyewitnesses were not mistaken.

What are the possibilities that Dr Jamieson's monitoring equipment was not picking up the levels of emission that eyewitness accounts were indicating? If it is accepted that dangerous chemicals were emitted through the various stacks and vents, a number of questions arise. Where did emissions go when they left the plant? How much of the toxic materials arrived at Hanrahan's farm? Could the levels arriving at the farm have caused the problems reported?

Angus Graham's report would indicate that, in those early days before the sides became entrenched, it was generally recognised that Hanrahan's farm was in the fall-out area for factory emissions, and that on hazy mornings they would be likely to land there. The significance of the boilerhouse plume on that occasion was not what it contained but that it indicated what might have been happening to other emissions. It was acting as a tracer. But, despite all the scientific testing, no tracer experiment was attempted.

Dermot Gleeson took up this issue with Richard Ruch, Merck's American meteorologist. He asked him if he had conducted any experiments with smoke or harmless chemicals as a test for the direction in which factory emissions might be carried. "You know the sort of thing I am talking about?"

"Yes."

"Could you?"

"Yes."

"It would show you where the smoke went?"

"Yes."

"That wasn't done?"

"No."

Angus Graham's observations were reflected in numerous accounts by people within a two-mile radius and usually north or east of the factory, which suggests that frequently clouds of emission took a somewhat erratic trajectory in the general direction of Hanrahan's farm, and tended to hit the ground in a patchwork formation.

Michael Hickey, a county council foreman and part-time farmer who lives half a mile north-east of the plant, was one of the residents who testified on Merck's behalf that, although he had detected some smells from the factory, he did not regard them as harmful. The last time had been a "fairly obnoxious smell" about two years previously, lasting five or six minutes, but neither he nor his family suffered any ill health, nor did he notice any damage to his potatoes or animals.

In July 1983 John Wallace was part of a group of farmers visiting a farm beside the Merck factory with their agricultural adviser. "When we arrived everything seemed to be fine, and suddenly this unpleasant smell hit us." The group was forced to abandon the work, and the following year Wallace described a further experience in a field two-and-a-half miles north-east of the factory, just beyond Ballycurkeen. His cattle all rose together suddenly and moved to the corner of the field with their heads in the air as if they were sniffing something. He himself detected nothing until he reached his car; as he began to drive on a route at right angles to the direction of the factory, he encountered a strong objectionable odour.

John Kehoe, who lives on a farm just north of the factory, said he had no problems but did get smells on occasion. "Maybe four or five years ago I got a smell on a couple of occasions. I was saving hay on an outside farm three years ago and I got a smell one day. I rang up the factory, and they were on holidays at the time. They were cleaning some containers or something like that, so since I didn't ever get a smell." Unwittingly, Kehoe was endorsing one of the charges made against the factory by John Hanrahan, who had claimed that even factory maintenance operations during the annual holiday gave rise to emissions.

John Callanan lives with his family directly south of Hanrahan's farm and east of the factory. When the odours got particularly intense he complained a number of times. "I have been milking my cows in the milking parlour and would have to send word to my wife to close all the windows. Otherwise the smell would continue inside after it disappeared outside. It would last for a few hours outside, but if you didn't have your windows closed you could have it all night inside."

Hanrahan's nearest neighbour, Tommy Rockett, described an occasion when he repeatedly drove in and out of a cloud of fumes as he harrowed a field. On another occasion he was driving along the road on a combine harvester. "It was a wet night. I was coming home. I had no cab on the combine and suddenly—there was a monitoring hut on the hill, and I met this bloody foul odour, and I woke up on the combine after fifty yards and I was gone through it. It came from the right. I owned the field on the right; I knew there was nothing there, the corn was cut . . . The wind and rain was coming from the factory side." During his leaf yeast study as part of the TCD investigation in 1982, Dr Paul Dowding spent some time walking the Ballydine area. On one excursion he walked through a bank of drifting odour several hundred yards wide, getting first-hand experience of the phenomenon he was trying to describe in court.

☐

Looking south across the Suir valley from the top of Slievenamon, 2,000 feet above sea level, the Comeragh mountain range rises to an equal height ten miles away in Co Waterford. The opposing mountains graduate down towards the river in folds, merging into lower hills, so that in the broad saucer shape between the two ranges there is a narrow "valley within a valley." Sitting on the floor of this valley is the Merck factory at Ballydine.

From this point the south side is steep and rises to 600 feet within a few hundred yards. The north side slopes gently upwards to a 600-foot ridge within two miles. When the sun goes down behind Slievenamon and the land cools on the northern folds of the valley, the air above the cooling land cools also. The heavy cooling air moves down the slope; and when the sun sinks further, the cool air also moves down the Glenpoer slopes on the south side. If the wind drops and the sky is clear, the cold air, undisturbed, slinks further down the sides of the valley, its moisture condensing into droplets of fog as the air cools and contracts. The longer the night, the higher the bank of cold air that slowly builds up: in summer it might go to fifty, perhaps a hundred feet; in winter it might rise to three hundred feet, and rest there like a huge lid on the valley. Meteorologists call this phenomenon an inversion.

The Merck plant, never sleeping, would go on through the night, puffing out its manifold emissions. In stable conditions the emissions would curl up like smoke from giant cigarettes, breaking slowly and diffusing into the air. Unable to rise, they would fan out to the sides, mixing with the stable air beneath the lid of the inversion. And there they would sit waiting for the dawn.

The sun would first warm up the land on the northern side of the valley, and as the land heated it would heat the air above it. The heated air would want to rise, and heavier, colder air would drop down to take its place. The inversion would begin to roll slowly up the north slope of the valley, fanning out sideways, still unable to rise above the main canopy of cold air until that rolled over too.

Inversions can be associated with light wind, up to ten miles an hour. If the wind came from the south-west it would push the breaking inversion towards the rising land. And the slow-moving bank of air containing Merck emissions would hit the ground at Ballycurkeen, just above the height of the incinerator stack, just level with the top of the scrubber stack, just below the level of the boilerhouse stack, licking its way around Hanrahan's farm and laying down a carpet of toxic particles on the grass.

Richard Ruch used a computer model to predict the points at which emissions from the stacks would hit the ground and at what concentrations. He installed a miniature weather centre at the factory, and collected data such as wind speed and direction for five months. He concluded that the concentrations arriving at Hanrahan's farm would be very low, and according to his data the conditions required for an inversion while the wind was blowing in Hanrahan's direction occurred for only 1½ per cent of the time in a year. Dowding argued that the device Ruch used was unable to measure wind accurately at low speeds, and so the method would not give an accurate indication of the frequency of inversions.

Another unknown was the height of the inversion, the column of stable air over the valley. This figure was important in arriving at concentrations, because the bigger the layer, the bigger the dilution of the contaminant mixing with it. Ruch had assumed a height that would include the emissions from all three stacks.

Ruch agreed that the invisible lid on the valley would have a funnelling effect, and with the ground rising to meet it, the plume would be compressed into as little as six feet at Hanrahan's, giving a high concentration of emissions at the farm. But a factor known as downwash would also have to be considered. This is caused when an obstruction interrupts the flow of the wind. It leads to aerodynamic turbulence or an eddying effect at the far side of the obstruction, tending to draw the wind towards ground level. Ruch insisted that the Merck process building would have this downwash effect on the incinerator plume on its way towards the Hanrahan farm, so that some of the contents of the plume would be drawn down on the land between the factory and the farm. However, he seems to have been somewhat selective in the data he used. He assumed that downwash from a building in the path of the incinerator plume would apply, but took no account of the downwash effects of the hills flanking the valley. This approach appeared to disregard the restricting effect of the hills on emissions as well their downwash effect on winds blowing across them. He assumed that none of the surrounding hills was higher than the top of the highest stack.

It also turned out that Ruch's computer model did not take account of the break-up of inversions, which is when the impact of emissions at the Hanrahan farm was likely to be greatest; neither did it make allowance for hydrochloric acid travelling as a mist as well as in the form of gas; nor did it include a measure of "wet deposits," the effect of rain washing pollutants out of the travelling plumes and onto the grass. In effect Ruch's model had calculated what the concentrations of emissions would be at one to two metres above the ground. According to Ruch the Merck emissions could not have arrived at Hanrahan's farm in significant concentrations after they left the factory. According to Dowding they probably did.

Assuming that emissions did arrive at the farm—and even the company admitted that some did—the next question is, how much? The standard Merck response was to take refuge in the findings of Dr Jamieson, who had concluded that the air in the Ballydine area met quality standards at all times. Merck produced an array of experts who testified that to get the kind of discomfort reported in humans and animals, the levels of acids and organics would need to have been several times higher than those measured by Jamieson.

The 24-hour averages measured by Jamieson were at levels that all the experts agreed could not be detected by the senses. But human and animal life would respond to peaks rather than averages. Jamieson therefore undertook a series of measurements to see whether acid concentrations were occasionally higher at certain times of the day than at others. The results were not significantly different from his earlier findings.

He also did another, more theoretical exercise. At about 7,000 micrograms per cubic metre, hydrochloric acid begins to cause irritation to the nose and throat and is not considered safe to work in. Working backwards, Jamieson made the assumption that this level arrived at the monitors on Hanrahan's farm and lasted for fifteen minutes, and that for the rest of the twenty-four hours the air was clear. This would give a 24-hour average of 75 micrograms per cubic metre. He found that this was exceeded on thirty-four occasions in the summer of 1981. In other words, if all the acid recorded that summer was hydrochloric acid, the irritation threshold could have been exceeded many times in short fifteen-minute bursts.

Of course this was hypothetical, but it showed at least that Jamieson's measurements did not rule out the possibility that short bursts of concentrated emissions were arriving at the farm.

The Merck team suggested that it was far-fetched to assume that all the acid measured by Jamieson arrived in such a short period. "Can I ask you first of all," Peter Shanley put it to Jamieson, "does the assumptions on which you base your calculations, is one of the assumptions that the air for the remaining 23 hours and 45 minutes of the day doesn't have a single microgram per metre cubed of SO_2 in it?"

"Yes, that would be the case."

"Having regard to the facts of the case, is it reasonable, a reasonable assumption?"

"All I can say is that it is generally accepted that the rural areas, the daily average concentration would be about 25 micrograms per cubic metre. It would be as much as that. My exercise is the worst possible case type of calculation, and in fact it is likely that—it is unlikely that there would be no acid vapour calculated over the remaining 23³/₄ hours."

The assumption that, apart from fifteen minutes, the remaining part of the day was entirely free of acid was hardly meant to be taken literally, but the Merck team made the most of it. It was simply a means of illustrating that the lion's share of the daily average could have come in as short a period as fifteen minutes. Even allowing for a background acid level of 25 micrograms, as suggested by Jamieson, there was ample room for the possibility of very high concentrations in fifteen minutes.

Dr MacSweeney had also presented calculations based on the assumption that the emissions arrived in a short period rather than over the course of the day. He chose an hour, and did calculations both for acids and organics using the highest measurements recorded by Dr Jamieson. None of the concentrations he calculated for the hour would have exceeded the threshold limit value (TLV)—the minimum level at which vapours would be irritating. MacSweeney added that Jamieson did not record solvents like methanol and ethanol, which are commonly used at the factory.

"The most likely materials to be emitted are the most volatile ones, which are the solvents, and indeed these are emitted in harmless low quantities both from the scrubber stack and from the incinerator. I would expect to find these at a location outside the factory before I would expect to find any other things that are used in the Merck, Sharp and Dohme factory."

However, Jamieson pointed out later that his monitors did not pick up water-soluble organics, like methanol, ethanol, or ethyl acetate. Jamieson repeatedly recommended the use of monitors that could measure peak concentrations.

Such an instrument might cost five or six thousand pounds, but the county council apparently felt this was too much to spend. It was suggested that if Hanrahan was serious about verifying peak concentrations he could have acquired such a device himself. However, if the cost was a deterrent to the county council, it hardly seems reasonable to expect a farmer to make the outlay. In any case it would have had to be operated at the factory, a location out of bounds to Hanrahan.

However, the actual emission levels measured by Jamieson on Hanrahan's farm and the levels predicted by Ruch's computer models displayed a remarkable similarity, well within acceptable limits for the air that humans and animals are breathing twenty-four hours a day. So how could such emissions have led to the symptoms being reported?

Merck produced a number of scientific witnesses to testify on the impact of acid and organic chemicals in the air on humans and animals. Dr John Widdicombe, professor of physiology at St George's Hospital Medical School, London, and a specialist on the response of the respiratory tract to inhaled irritants, set out the concentrations that would be needed in the air to cause the kind of symptoms he was told were reported in the Ballydine area. For hydrochloric acid, 7,000 micrograms per cubic metre would cause immediate irritation to the nose and throat. For sulphur dioxide it would be 5,000. The highest measured concentrations on the Hanrahan farm were 51 micrograms per cubic metre for hydrochloric acid and 159 for sulphur dioxide.

Asked by Peter Shanley whether in his opinion the animal and human health complaints could have been caused by the measured levels of irritant gases, Widdicombe told the court, "It seems to me that in terms of the human health complaints the concentrations recorded in the Jamieson report are so much below the general accepted value it is unlikely that that is so. In terms of animals, although laboratory animals have been studied in these tests I don't think farm animals have been. And I think it is reasonable to suppose that all mammals will behave in the same way, have the same response . . ."

In cross-examination Dermot Gleeson asked him what symptoms he would look for if he suspected a high concentration of irritants.

"I would ask questions about the possible acute exposure to high concentrations, such as running eyes, coughing—"

"Running eyes and coughing?"

"Yes; perhaps stuffiness of the nose. If the population did not show any signs of these acute responses then one would have to look into the long term to see if there were any chronic changes developing."

Widdicombe had not been to the Ballydine area, and he admitted that he had neither heard nor read most of the eyewitness evidence. He based his testimony mainly on a reading of the evidence selected by Merck of the other doctors in the case, the Jamieson reports, and the court evidence of John Hanrahan.

"Do you agree, so far as they go in terms of reports of symptoms relating to eyes, mouth, and nose, the reports you have read are typical of the irritant effects?"

"They are consistent with irritants, yes."

Gleeson went on to outline Ger Clancy's description of feeling burning and irritation at the same time that Hanrahan's animals were coughing when he was testing them.

"I cannot speak for the cows, but I think the man, his sense of burning and coughing would be consistent with the high concentration of irritants."

It is generally accepted that hydrochloric acid is confined to industrial situations: it is not expected to get out into the environment. The threshold limit value of 7,000 micrograms per cubic metre is the level that must not be exceeded on the factory floor, eight hours a day, forty hours a week; but threshold limit values are not stringent enough for the ambient air, and they have no application to children, to people with respiratory difficulties, or to animals. Much more severe standards are set for ambient air: a limit one-fortieth of the TLV, or 125 micrograms per cubic metre over twenty-four hours, is sometimes used. The German standard on the other hand requires that even in the work-place the concentration not exceed 100 micrograms for any thirty-minute period. If all the acid Jamieson measured at Hanrahan's farm was hydrochloric acid, the levels would have exceeded the German standard repeatedly, mainly in June 1981.

Professor Widdicombe pointed to the highest measurements for hydrochloric acid, 51 micrograms per cubic metre. But Dermot Gleeson put it to him that it would be a different matter if it all arrived in a short period rather than over over twenty-four hours, for example if it arrived in ten minutes. "What figure would that give us, something near 8,000?"

"Yes."

"There is no doubt that if it arrived in ten minutes the TLV ceiling would be exceeded?"

"Yes."

The only toxicologist to be called was Dr Andrew Salmon of the London School of Tropical Medicine. He testified on Merck's behalf that the toxicity of chemicals depends on the concentration and the duration of exposure. "In my opinion there is no relationship between the animal and human effects at concentrations at which they are reported by Dr Jamieson to occur." He added that there is no necessary relationship between the toxic effect of airborne chemicals and the level at which they can be smelt or felt. He cited the example of hydrogen sulphide, which has a strong smell of rotten eggs at quite low concentration but is not toxic until much higher levels are reached; on the other hand hydrogen cyanide is highly toxic long before it can be detected by smell.

Jamieson's study identified twenty-four different organic compounds in the Ballydine air, albeit at low concentrations, and the test indicated the presence of up to fifty others that it was unable to identify. Among them may have been some highly toxic materials that were undetectable by the senses but were quietly poisonous.

It is probable that three types of emission from the factory were confused and interlinked in the Ballydine area. There were unpleasant odours caused mainly by the by-products of sulindac; there was irritation and respiratory distress from materials such as hydrochloric acid and sulphur dioxide, followed or preceded by the smell of these materials; and there were organic solvents such as toluene, chloroform, and monochlorobenzene, which may have been accompanied by small amounts of highly toxic agents like phosgene and dioxins.

It is tempting to conclude that the Hanrahans' problems were caused entirely by this last category, which would reconcile the opposing testimony of eyewitnesses and scientific measurements; but that would mean that the irritation and respiratory distress reported by the Hanrahans and others would have to be rejected as a figment of their imagination. It would mean their animals did not have weeping eyes and runny noses, did not have coughing and breathing difficulty, did not have sore udders, or refuse to eat the grass, or vomit when they did eat, or show symptoms of lung damage.

To return to the three questions asked at the beginning of this chapter, where did the emissions go when they left the plant? Nobody knows exactly. Some of them were carried to Hanrahan's farm at Ballycurkeen. There is no dispute about that: it is a matter of degree.

It is in attempting to answer the second question—how much of the toxic materials arrived at Hanrahan's farm?—that the two sides take opposing views. The answer to the third question—could the levels arriving at the farm have caused the problems reported?—depends on the answer to the second. If we accept the answer suggested by the air monitoring techniques of Jamieson, the predictions of Ruch and the opinions of Merck's other scientific experts we would have to say no, the levels of emissions that arrived could not have caused the problems reported.

Paradoxically, it is the testimony of these Merck experts that invites a positive answer. According to them, the symptoms reported could not have been caused without concentrations several times higher than those measured. They said each cubic metre of air would have to contain 7,000 micrograms of hydrochloric acid or 5,000 micrograms of sulphur dioxide to cause irritation. Jamieson's highest measurement was thirty times below these levels. Yet Jamieson acknowledged in his second report that "residents were occasionally subjected to short exposures of factory vapours which may have an unpleasant odour or may irritate the skin and eyes." The Lynch report described a similar phenomenon, leading to "irritation of the mucous membranes, lachrymation and unpleasant odours." From Professor Widdicombe's evidence it is clear that Jamieson's figures could not have caused these symptoms; so the concentration *must* have been at least 5,000 or 7,000 during those short exposures. Unwittingly, Jamieson was confirming that, from time to time, the air contained a much higher level of acid than he had measured. Here is the missing link.

In this light it is easier to accept Paul Dowding's portrayal of weather patterns in the valley funnelling emissions straight to the farm on the side of the hill, and easier to conclude that a high enough concentration of emissions must have arrived to cause the problems. Otherwise the compelling testimony of so many eyewitness accounts would have to be rejected. The conclusion must be that Merck, Sharp and Dohme emissions were responsible for the problems at the Hanrahan farm, "on the balance of probability," an expression that was to be heard again.

13

FARM MANAGEMENT

The first Lynch report to the Department of Agriculture investigation was submitted to Brian Lenihan in October 1982. It established no link between the factory and the Hanrahans' problems, and concluded that these were more likely to be due to factors internal to the farm. It recommended that no further state resources be spent until Hanrahan made available the results of his private testing and certain other data. This data was not forthcoming, and the Lynch team sought other sources of information about the farm.

The general tone of the final report was substantially the same as that of the earlier one. It said the available evidence did not support the conclusion that emissions from the Merck factory were causing human and animal health problems. Some reported problems were normal occurrences, and others were linked to husbandry practices. In a nutshell, the Hanrahans' problems were mainly due to bad farm management.

Dr Mark Lynch and his team had undertaken an exhaustive study of Hanrahan's herd file in the Department of Agriculture in a futile effort to establish animal movement patterns on the farm. From Avonmore Co-op,without Hanrahan's knowledge or approval, they got details of milk sold and supplies bought. The report admitted that assumptions had had to be made in building up a picture of the herd changes, as animal counts included in the file were compiled only at the time of the annual herd test. The file contained no information about births, deaths, sales or purchases of animals between tests.

From the file the Lynch team had compiled a table showing the number of times brucellosis tests were inconclusive. Lynch refused to comment when Dermot Gleeson suggested that inconclusive tests for brucellosis have no significance.

"If you can't comment on those matters," Gleeson asked, "why did you put that table together, and what significance do you say this has to the relationships between Hanrahan's cattle and Merck, Sharp and Dohme? What does that table contribute?"

"That table was prepared in the context of our analysis of the herd file. The information of this nature was properly brought to the attention of the senior veterinary officers concerned in this, with disease eradication, and no further comment I can make. No further comment."

"You presented it in court. You agree with me it has nothing at all to do with anything with which this court is concerned?"

"It was contained in our analysis and it derived from our analysis of the herd file. The work we had completed was presented in our report, provided to both plaintiffs and defendants in the early days of this period."

"If you say it has significance, any significance in the context of the controversy with which this court is concerned, will you now tell us what that significance is?"

"The only significance is that it is a record of what the herd file shows in this regard," Lynch responded, implying that the analysis was undertaken merely for its own sake.

The report attempted to explain excessively high animal death rates. Calf deaths at birth or just afterwards, it said, fell within the normal range, and the fact that mortality on the farm had increased could be due to changes in husbandry practice and the increase in herd size. Weanling deaths were due to a severe outbreak of hoose in 1981, again indicating poor husbandry practice, which could also explain the generally poor growth rate in the herd.

Ten deaths in a 120-cow herd in a period of eighteen months were more difficult to explain. That represented a mortality rate of over 5 per cent, where less than 1 per cent would be usual. But again the report found that three of the animals had not been in the herd in the preceding herd test. (The Lynch team were not aware that three sick cows had been sent to UCD veterinary college for slaughter and post-mortem examination. Although not farm deaths, they were included in the death list on the grounds that they would have died on the farm anyway.)

Otherwise the report suggested that cow deaths might be associated with calving difficulties, hoose, or old age. The study of the herd file had revealed that up to 20 per cent of the cows were over eight years old, the average age at which cows are culled. Old age was also offered as a possible reason for the unusually high number of twins, but the report said that "sixteen sets of twins would not be very unusual in two calving seasons in a herd of 120 cows." In fact twelve sets of twins had been born in three months. The team were unable to comment on calf deformities except to suggest that they may have been due to inbreeding.

From the data made available to them they were able to reach the general conclusion that the herd had a high degree of fertility and that milk yield was well above the average. But there was a rapid build-up in animal numbers between 1978 and 1983, and the implication was that Hanrahan's standard of animal husbandry had not improved apace. They said also that the culling rate was too low.

"The basic pattern that emerged," Lynch told the court, "was of a significant increase in numbers of animals over the years, a dramatic increase in the numbers of animals, a large increase in the numbers of cows. They increased by some 62 per cent in this period."

The number of livestock units on the farm (adult equivalents) increased from 200 to 275 over five years, an annual increase of 7 per cent—hardly the kind of expansion to stretch the abilities of most farmers. At the time the Department of Agriculture itself was calling on farmers for stock increases of that magnitude.

"I want to suggest to you," Gleeson put to Lynch in cross-examination, "that saying there was a rapid build-up was a gross distortion of what you knew to be the truth, as it is not fairly representative of the situation on this farm?"

"On the contrary." What they saw as the rapid build-up of animals led the Lynch team to conclude that the farm was overstocked, and a study of the data supplied by Avonmore indicated that grass production was limited by low fertiliser application.

"Do you think that it is consistent to find that the farm was overcrowded, the animals underfed, and yet they were exceptionally fertile and good milk yields? That doesn't hang together?"

"The detailed analysis of the sort that would permit the type of answering you are trying to elicit would be possible, I would say, had we had detailed statements, detailed information on the amounts of hay and silage and on the amounts and type, particular type, of feeding concentrates. Since we did not have the benefit of that information we could not comment further on that aspect."

"You were prepared to say your belief was that the animals did not have enough feed?"

"No, we made the statement, if memory serves me correctly, in the report that the fertiliser regime used and the nutritional standards established in 1982 would indicate that grass and forage would be in short supply. We did not have sufficient information on whether forage had been purchased or whether grassland had been leased. That was information that would be essential to draw the sort of conclusions one way or the other you are referring to."

In fact Hanrahan had rented 23 acres for grazing in 1981 and 1982 and the equivalent of 100 acres in 1983. If adjustments are made for the rented land, the most intensive stocking rate for the farm would have come to 1 acre per livestock unit, rather than the estimate of 0.75 suggested by the report. This would not be unusually high for an intensive dairy farm like Hanrahan's.

"Did you ever walk around this farm yourself?"

"No."

"Did any of the other people on your team walk around it?"

"I understand they did."

"Which of them told you that there was evidence that there wasn't enough feed?"

"No-one told me that at all. Had they done so it would have been, in any event, less impressive than the hard information—hard subject to the limitations I outlined—that our analysis revealed."

Gleeson went on to list the evidence of observers like Michael English and Peter Dougan, who had said the animals were well fed. "Do you feel happy by that analysis, against eyewitness accounts, against someone like Mr English, who one would regard as reliable?"

"I would always rely on detailed analysis and investigation as being far preferable," Lynch continued to defend the battlements of science, "far more reliable, and certainly an indicator of what is happening, than a subjective observation of any man, no matter how well informed."

"The average farmer who is simply looking at the grass and the cows eating enough of it," Gleeson persisted, "would be better advised to get someone like you to do an analysis of how much fertiliser he had purchased that year to see whether his cows are hungry or not?"

"Clearly."

"Isn't it absurd?"

"It is absurd that we had to use such an indirect means to investigate a problem where more direct means would have been far more efficacious in resolving the problem."

It was difficult to argue with that conclusion.

Gleeson moved on to deal with Lynch's concentration

on feed and fertiliser in the context of the main problem. "Dr Lynch, you are making a great deal of fuss about the information you had about feed levels. Can I suggest to you in the context of trying to see whether the emissions from Merck, Sharp and Dohme were poisoning these animals, wondering whether they had enough NPK [fertiliser], that you were not addressing the main problem?"

"I could not answer that."

"You never addressed it and have never addressed the main problem?"

"I would agree with your main statement, that I have not been permitted to address the main problem. Had we been permitted to complete an analysis and quantification of the problems then, as had again and again been offered by the department, a detailed investigation following purchase of the animals would have been followed. It is unfortunate that the services of the various state agencies made available weren't availed of."

The Lynch report provided a ready-made defence for Merck. The defence strategy was to concentrate on what they argued were John Hanrahan's limitations as a farm manager and on inconsistencies in the family's record-keeping. In this way they would be able to find internal reasons for the animal health problems and to argue at the same time that a lot fewer animals died than the Hanrahans were claiming. It was a two-pronged offensive, built around a number of expert witnesses.

The sides produced a bewildering array of conflicting farm management data. Figures prepared by Hanrahan's accountants show cattle deaths for the period covered by litigation (1 January 1981 to 30 June 1984) as 138, which coincided with Selina Hanrahan's death list.

Merck's chief agricultural witness was Dr Nicholas Bielenberg of Stewarts Ltd, farm management consultants. He produced an extensive set of figures, based on the same data, though some of it came from different sources.

Bielenberg's company got access to Hanrahan's herd file under circumstances that further convinced the

Hanrahan team that the Department of Agriculture was less than impartial. Dr Lynch was subpoenad to appear in court as a Merck witness *ducis tecum,* which obliged him to make his documents available in court only, not beforehand. He told the court that the department had advice from the Attorney General that his reports could be made available to anyone who sought them once the case began. This advice did not extend to the Hanrahan herd file, a confidential document; but this was made available to Merck, and Lynch discussed it with Bielenberg. The Hanrahans felt the department was helping the Merck case by handing over the file, vindicating their earlier decision to withhold their veterinary consultants' findings from the department. (The family's suspicions were reinforced two years later when the department refused to make the same herd file—their own file—available to them to prepare for the Supreme Court case. On instructions from the minister, the file was eventually handed over after the case.)

In any event the herd file figures coincided with a list kept independently by the Hanrahans; and Bielenberg also got information from Avonmore Co-op on milk sales and materials purchased, again without Hanrahan's consent. In addition he had access to the same stock lists and records of sales and purchases as Hanrahan's accountant.

But from essentially the same information the two accountants came up with strikingly different results, the most notable being the number of deaths. Bielenberg concluded that only 65 animals had died during the period covered. He had used a lower figure for the opening stock, lower figures for births and purchases, and a higher figure for the closing stock.

A fundamental part of the Merck defence was to cast doubt on the accuracy of the family's record-keeping, and Selina's death list in particular. The first line of attack was to establish that mortality was already high on the farm before 1981.

Up to 1978 it was Mary Hanrahan who looked after the livestock, and each year Mary kept records in an account book. She testified that deaths were so few that she could count them on her fingers—not more than ten a year. At the end of 1980 Selina began to compile the list of deaths and other developments from information supplied by John and Charles Hanrahan, Mary Hanrahan's nephew Michael Armstrong, and Pat Quinlan. The information came from diaries kept by herself and the others, from various pieces of paper and from direct communication. She transcribed it first into folders and a book known as Book V before finally photocopying all the information into the Red Book. The pieces of paper were then discarded, but the diaries, folders and Book V were retained.

As far as Merck were concerned, Selina's Red Book had to be undermined. They began to examine its contents, and Selina, who had just spent time in hospital in intensive care with lung problems, came under severe cross-examination.

On the fifth day of the hearing Mr Justice Keane ordered the Hanrahans to make a supplementary affidavit of discovery of any records of animal mortality. This led to the production of the diaries filled in by the various people, including Selina herself, perhaps a dozen diaries altogether. Some of them had been used as notebooks for assorted information and personal details.

It became apparent that there were a number of inconsistencies both within and between diaries. They did not all have the same entries for the same days, and, as might be expected, the same events were often recorded in different ways. A lot of court time was spent in an attempt to explain the inconsistencies; but the Merck defence homed in on one incident. As Selina was looking through the documents preparing them for court, she made some minor amendments to her 1981 diary for completeness. Inevitably the amendments were noticed, and Tom Smyth was forced to raise it with Selina when she was recalled to the witness box.

"Did you, in fact, make certain alterations in the diaries since the beginning of this case?"

"I finished off a couple of sentences." Selina had noticed that entries in the Red Book were more elaborate in a few cases than in her original diary. This happened because some of the details came from other people's diaries and from information she was given orally. She saw no harm in amending her own diary to include the more elaborate description in the Red Book. In other instances, taking the information from the Red Book, she completed sentences in the diary. The amendments made no material difference to the information in the diary, but they helped the Merck team to undermine the document as an original record of events. It was a stroke of luck for the defence, which they were not slow to exploit.

Apart from the alterations to her 1981 diary, a number of double entries were noticed in the Red Book. "24 April 1981—Cow number 30 had twin heifers . . . 24 May 1981—Cow number 30 had twin heifers."

"Do I understand it to be the case," Peter Shanley asked, "at least a month after April the twenty-fourth, you were going through your little bits of paper and you found reference to cow 30 had a dead heifer and you decided to put it in for that particular date on which you found the note?"

"It could happen. I had many pieces of paper and diaries and [I did it] to make sure I wasn't making a mistake anywhere."

Shanley went on to draw attention to an entry crossed out in her 1981 diary for 25 April and re-entered a month later. Selina explained that the entry was crossed out when she discovered it on the wrong page, but Shanley persisted.

"For that particular Saturday, the twenty-fifth of April, the entire reference to Mr de Lacy and 531 calf are written with the same pen, whereas on the twenty-fifth—"

"They are not."

"The entire of that was written with the same pen."

"They are written with two different pens."

"A different pen on each date—?"

"I don't want to interrupt," Mr Justice Keane intervened,

"but I have to see the original on this point. Could I see the original? The photocopy doesn't bring up these things." He examined the diary and confirmed Selina's version of events.

Another incident related to the death of cow 277 and her calf. "10 January, 1981—Cow 277 died . . . 10 January, 1981—Cow 277's calf died."

Selina could not remember whether she had been told of the death or had taken it from a farm diary. Having established that she had not actually seen the cow and calf die on the farm, Shanley got to the point. "This particular cow, which you have told the defendants in your notice for particulars died with its calf, in fact went to the factory. It did not die on the farm."

"That may be so, but why did she go to the factory?" John Hanrahan had called the vet, Martin O'Gorman, when cow 277 was eight or nine days overdue and unable to calve. O'Gorman found that the calf was dead and the cow could not be saved, so he advised Hanrahan to send her for slaughter. The factory would pay at least a salvage price for a live animal but would not accept a dead one.

Cow 277 was the fourth entry, and was the only example of its kind. It was made just after Selina had begun to compile the list, when the type of deaths to be recorded had not been fully decided.

The Merck team pointed out a number of other discrepancies. Pat Quinlan's diaries recorded fewer deaths than Selina's list; but it is clear from both Quinlan's diaries and his evidence that his diaries were incomplete. There were long periods when he was absent due to illness, mainly chest trouble. However, the death list did include the eleven animals killed for the post-mortem examination, on the grounds that all animals dying on the farm should be recorded. While the animals concerned were in such poor health that they might have died in any case, it could hardly be argued that the deaths were spontaneous. However, the Hanrahan team decided to include every farm animal that died.

There was clearly some element of double counting; but no amount of investigation could prove that the family had fabricated the deaths of seventy-three animals—the number that separated Selina's figures from those of Bielenberg. To do that they would have needed the acquiescence of Tom de Lacy and his partners, their agricultural adviser, their accountants, and their solicitors.

In his closing submission Dermot Gleeson accepted that the diaries were by no means a perfect record but rather what might be expected from people who were not accustomed to keeping records for court purposes. If they had been fabricated the massive amount of mundane and personal detail would not have been included—detail that the defence accepted or rejected as it suited them. The records had to be accepted as they were. "They are not something the Institute of Secretaries or anyone like that would want to admire, but in that very fact, in their very ineptitude, lies their truth."

According to the defence, the problems could be traced to the beginning of John Hanrahan's tenure as manager in 1978, when he embarked on an ambitious expansion plan. It was Merck's case that Hanrahan allowed the farm to become overstocked and underfertilised and to be otherwise mismanaged, because of his preoccupation with their activities at Ballydine. As a consequence the underfed animals fell prey to the chain of diseases and health conditions reported.

Figures found among Hanrahan's documents and submitted in court as part of Bielenberg's presentation showed that stocking density on the farm was already high when Hanrahan took over. In 1970 the farm had 1.08 acres for each livestock unit. Thereafter the density dropped slightly, to 1.14 in 1978, the kind of level being achieved by top-rank dairy farmers at the time.

However, all the calculations show that there was an increase in stocking density on Hanrahan's farm from 1981 onwards. His agricultural adviser, Michael English, warned him about it, and it is clear that Hanrahan himself was unhappy. "Over 1981 and 1982 and indeed 1983 the stocking rate was not of our own choice. It was forced on us, and when the finance that was available and the money that was available, we did it to the best of our ability. There was a meeting in Ballycurkeen on the twenty-seventh—I think it was September the twenty-seventh—and the question was raised, what would happen to the surplus stock? Our vet, Mr de Lacy, it would be against his wishes that these stocks would be sold for human consumption . . ."

Bielenberg argued that a very high level of soil fertility would be needed to reach the stocking intensity Hanrahan was attempting. Both An Foras Talúntais and the Lynch report had established that phosphate and potassium application were too low on the farm and nitrogen probably too high. Bielenberg came to the same conclusion.

When the trouble began, Hanrahan had chosen to spend his limited resources on nitrogen rather than phosphate and potassium, on the grounds that nitrogen gave immediate results. It was a choice made by many farmers when cash was low. Bielenberg argued that another choice Hanrahan had made in the circumstances was even more unwise economically: deciding to feed extra meals. He would have got much higher return on his money if he spent it on phosphates and potash fertiliser. But the problem was that Hanrahan's cows were rejecting the grass (as were Tommy Rockett's at the time). There was little point in wasting fertiliser on grass that the animals were refusing.

Further problems arose when Hanrahan began to harvest his silage at the end of May. After a few days in the pit both the silage and its effluent developed a repulsive smell, and Hanrahan decided to have samples tested. For this reason, his second cut of silage was delayed and had reached an advanced stage of maturity at harvesting in July, a fact that would reduce the amount of digestible feed in it.

The normal test for feeding value showed that the silage was poor, but this test was not able to detect chemical contamination. When the cows went back on silage feeding for the winter the problems continued. They refused to eat the silage, and Hanrahan was forced to continue feeding extra meals. The excessive meal feeding continued throughout 1982 and 1983, but milk yield was now falling despite it. Hanrahan's accountants estimated the total cost of extra feeding over the period at just under £40,000 and lost milk yield at £68,000.

Reflecting the Lynch report suggestion, the defence claimed that Hanrahan's birth defects and abnormalities could be due to inbreeding caused by inadequate records. Hanrahan tried to explain that none of his bulls were home-bred and that detailed breeding records were unnecessary because of his own system of ear tagging, which he had introduced in 1972. In addition to the Department of Agriculture identity tag each cow had a large ear tag with a number and a letter, which allowed anyone on the farm to tell its age and pedigree. When bulls joined the herd they were numbered also to avoid inbreeding.

Records of mating were kept each year to allow the cows' calving dates to be predicted; but those records were not retained beyond a year. Hanrahan explained that the system had foundered in 1983 and 1984 when the cows began to show erratic mating behaviour. But a breakdown in 1983 and 1984 could hardly explain deformities in 1981 and 1982. In fact breeding aberrations are one of the lasting residues of Hanrahan's difficulties. While most other symptoms had disappeared by the late nineteen-eighties, the cows were continuing to come in heat at irregular intervals, and there were occasional birth defects.

Merck's dilemma in attempting to explain what was happening is perhaps best illustrated by the contradictory positions forced upon Dr Bielenberg. He argued that the farm had above average milk yields and stocking rate and unremarkable mortality levels. At the same time he had to explain how such a farm was overstocked and underfertilised and made bad silage, and how dairy cows getting 25 per cent more meal than required were underfed.

This predicament was reflected in the equally contradictory nature of the arguments by Merck's veterinary witnesses. Professor Pirie suggested that the herd was afflicted by as many as twenty different health problems, principally the kind that could be caused by bad management. But in early 1985 Dr Kevin Dodd found a good, well-laid-out farm with healthy animals in the kind of condition he would expect at that time of year. The list of symptoms for which Pirie was giving veterinary reasons could only have disappeared by the time of Dodd's visit if they had an external cause that was no longer there in early 1985.

In March 1984 the Lynch report was recommending "that it be recognised that while the information available is indicative of problems reported being due to or associated with factors indigenous to the Hanrahan farm and its management, the possibility remains that external factors may be causing or contributing to at least some of the problems reported."

Despite the Lynch emphasis the conclusion must be that a farmer who had been able to produce milk at a level of efficiency in line with the best farms in the country would scarcely begin to behave irrationally and carelessly and treat his animals to expensive and unnecessary feed over several years if confronted by farming problems alone. Someone familiar with bad weather and disease as the occupational hazards of farming would have dealt with such setbacks without losing his sense of perspective. There had to be an external factor, and there was one just down the road.

14

ACCORDING TO LAW

"This is a case which will last some time and may have a certain degree of complexity associated with it, but the basic facts of the case are relatively straightforward."

It was 11.00 a.m. on Wednesday 20 February 1985, three years after the Hanrahans had issued their first writ. Tom Smyth, senior counsel, was opening the High Court case on their behalf. "My clients have a family farm, 265-odd acres, at Ballycurkeen, Co Tipperary. Mrs Hanrahan senior has been on the farm for forty-odd years, and her son John, who is married to the third plaintiff, Selina, is a man who is presently thirty-six years old.

"In or about 1977 my clients did notice certain disturbances in the animals," Smyth lapsed into the archaic idiom of litigation, "but didn't put a great deal of thought upon this or in any way associate it with the defendants." He began to chronicle the sequence of events that led them to the courtroom. Below the judge sat the court clerk and stenographer. The solicitors occupied the first bench at floor level facing the body of the court. In the first rank facing the bench were the barristers: Kevin Liston, Peter Shanley and Nicholas Butler for Merck, and across the aisle Tom Smyth flanked by his colleagues Dermot Gleeson and Dan Herbert.

Mary, John and Selina Hanrahan sat side by side in the public benches towards the back of the court, struggling to catch exchanges, clearly overawed by the panoply of the law on this first day. Across the aisle, equally at odds with the acoustics, was the Merck management team, including Declan Buckley, David MacSweeney, and John Condon. Both sides would be joined intermittently by assorted witnesses and advisers as the case developed. Sixty-one witnesses would be called, ranging from the Hanrahan family and their neighbours with eyewitness accounts to Dr John Peterkin of Portsmouth Polytechnic, who treated the court to a discourse on gas chromatography and mass spectroscopy.

"The purpose of this action, primarily," Smyth continued, "is to protect the plaintiffs' interests. The defendant is part of a large, highly successful international pharmaceutical company which spends large sums of money in carrying out the art of processing and recovery in its operation."

To establish nuisance, the plaintiffs have to show that, on the balance of probability, over a substantial period of time they have suffered as a result of the way the defendants conducted their business. There is no need to prove that the defendants were negligent. Plaintiffs can also resort to a rule established in 1866 in the case of *Rylands* v. *Fletcher* that anyone who keeps a dangerous substance on their land is responsible for the damage it causes if it escapes; to succeed under this formula it is sufficient to show that the escape of material happened once. The Hanrahans' legal team set out to show that harmful emissions from Merck arrived at the farm repeatedly, reasoning that if they could prove repeated occurrences their case would succeed both on grounds of nuisance and under the 1866 rule.

Making their claim for nuisance, they referred to a careful statement of the principles involved by Mr Justice Gannon in *Halpin and Others* v. *Tara Mines* (1976). A party asserting that he had sustained damage must establish that such damage was caused by the nuisance as alleged. If he alleges that the nuisance has interfered with his enjoyment of property and caused personal discomfort, his evidence must show that the damage was of a kind that would diminish the comfort and enjoyment of a reasonable person living in the same locality.

Normally it is up to the party making an accusation to prove that he has been injured. There is no obligation on the defendant to prove that such injury did not arise as a result of his behaviour. However, exceptions to this rule are allowed in certain circumstances, and Dermot Gleeson argued that this was such a case. The plaintiffs did not meet the defendants on equal terms in capacity for scientific research and general financial resources. "There is no doubt that the question of onus of proof in a case alleging environmental pollution is of crucial significance, because the polluters are, characteristically, large, substantial corporations which, of their nature, have convenient and free access to scientific information of a highly pertinent kind. The plaintiffs in this case, and plaintiffs characteristically, although not necessarily universally, are persons who have no knowledge of these matters and, more importantly, have no ready access to knowledge, in the sense that they cannot, without commencing an action, discover what goes on in the defendants' premises; and in many cases, including this, even when an action is brought, discovering precisely what goes on inside the walls can pose serious difficulties."

If the Hanrahans could show that the quality of the air at their farm had been altered by emissions from the Merck factory, it should then be up to the company to show that such alterations were harmless as a matter of reasonable scientific certainty. It would be unjust and unreasonable to expect a farmer and his family to shoulder such a burden of proof.

Gleeson cited a number of cases where the burden of proof had been shifted from the plaintiff to the defendant because the defendant had peculiar knowledge of the subject of the complaint. He went on to suggest that in essence the nature of the Hanrahans' complaints were against breaches of their constitutional rights to bodily integrity and private property.

Kevin Liston for Merck rejected the notion that there

were grounds for shifting the burden of proof to his client, arguing that simply because they were feeling discomfort did not give Hanrahans the right to pick on the factory down the road and expect them to prove that they were not responsible. "If one were to take this principle that Mr Gleeson suggested, that follows that once there is something that makes me uncomfortable, I can't say what it is, it is air coming from one of the chimneys around here, and I think I will select X and let X disprove it."

The first twenty-one days were taken up with a presentation of the Hanrahans' case, beginning with evidence from the three plaintiffs. There were seven other lay witnesses: Hanrahan's cousin Michael Armstrong, the long-serving assistant Pat Quinlan, and five neighbours. The four vets of Tom de Lacy's practice, the county council vet Peter Dougan and the Canadian pathologist Dr James Neufeld made a total of six vets testifying for the Hanrahans. Other witnesses included three medical doctors, two agricultural advisers, three scientists, two accountants, a loss adjuster, and an auctioneer.

The court adjourned for six weeks and resumed on 29 April to hear the defence. This began with the evidence of six Merck staff, including Declan Buckley, general manager, and Dr David MacSweeney, head of technical services. There were nine Ballydine residents, including five farmers, and then a succession of experts: Dr Ian Jamieson of An Foras Forbartha, Dr Ken Macken of the IIRS, and Dr Mark Lynch and Pat Crowe of the Department of Agriculture. Merck also called four other vets, three medical doctors, a botanist, a toxicologist, an agricultural consultant, and two meteorologists.

The Hanrahan team would have wanted the opportunity to cross-examine a number of other witnesses not called by Merck, such as county council officers and members of Merck staff like Frank Wyatt who had dealt with their complaints. If they called these witnesses themselves they would have been forced to examine them directly rather than cross-examine.

In his closing submission Dermot Gleeson argued that the Hanrahans were entitled to special damages, including the loss of milk and beef sales and reduced value of stock. Apart from the question of an injunction they were also entitled to exemplary damages. Closing statements were completed on 4 July, and Mr Justice Keane delivered his verdict a month later.

Addressing first the submission that the onus of proof be shifted to the defendants, he said the case did not fall within any of the well-established exceptions that warranted such a transfer. The Hanrahans were able to elicit substantial information on the manufacturing processes before the trial by the use of discovery and interrogatories, and they were thoroughly investigated during the case.

Furthermore, he said, it was perfectly within the competence of the plaintiffs to establish, by appropriate scientific measurements, any degree of pollution that might exist on their lands. There was no case for deviating from the basic rule that the legal burden of proof rested on the party complaining.

On animal health, the judge said it was clear beyond doubt that there was a decline in the health of the herd on the Hanrahan farm in the years from 1977 onwards. Evidence from a wide range of witnesses had shown that this decline was accompanied by coughing, streaming eyes, and running noses. He was less sure about the level of cattle mortality or about Selina's death list. Assessing the accountants' attempts at estimating the number of deaths from incomplete data, he favoured those of Dr Nicholas Bielenberg, who had taken into account both the stocktaking recorded by the Hanrahans and the information on the Department of Agriculture's herd file.

But he could not disregard the evidence of de Lacy and his partners that there appeared to be an increase in cattle mortality from 1978 onwards. So he concluded that there was an increase in mortality but that it was unquantifiable, because no records were available for the years before 1978 for comparison. In fact such records had been made available.

He accepted evidence of increased abortions, unusually high twinning, stillbirths, and deformities, as well as the accounts of sore udders, but felt the reports of stampeding and overgrown hooves were not significant. Likewise he did not accept the claim that milk yield had fallen.

As regards human health, Keane said it was remarkable that the Hanrahan family attended a number of doctors over the years but that only one had given evidence on their behalf, and no explanation for this failure to give evidence was offered. He could only conclude that, had they been called to testify, they would have been unable to say about Selina Hanrahan that she suffered from anything other than gynaecological problems of a distressing but well-established nature, the opinion offered by the defendants.

However, he entirely accepted the evidence of Professor Muiris Fitzgerald on John Hanrahan's air flow obstruction. "I conclude that there is no reliable evidence of significant ill health during the relevant years in the case of any of the members of the Hanrahan household other than Mr Hanrahan himself. In his case, the value of the evidence is significantly reduced by the absence of any evidence from his general practitioner. There was, however, no basis for the suggestion advanced in the closing stages of the case that he might himself have taken quantities of bromine in some form in order to produce misleading results." (The Hanrahan team apparently decided not to call the general practitioners because, unable to get to the root of the problems, the doctors themselves had referred the family to specialists, whose evidence was regarded as incorporating the views of the GPs.)

Keane accepted the evidence of unusual plant damage on the Hanrahan farm as described by Dr Paul Dowding but decided, on Jamieson's evidence, that the corrosion of farm buildings reported was in no way unusual scientifically.

The next question therefore was whether the plaintiffs had established, as a matter of probability, that the deterioration in animal health, John Hanrahan's illness and the damage to plant life were attributable to emissions of toxic gases and vapours from the defendants' factory. In this context the evidence of the monitoring of such gases on the farm was crucial.

The judge took a rather sceptical view of Dr Geoffrey Buck's contribution. The lichen study, showing evidence of pollution in the valley, was devalued by Dr Denis Brown's clearly expressed opinion that Buck's method was faulty. His animal hair study suffered from similar defects. It was devalued also by evidence, which the judge accepted, that for much of the critical time bromine was not used in the factory processes.

The only other scientific measurements of toxic gases available, Keane said, were those of Jamieson. "Those measurements quite simply lend no support to the plaintiffs' case. On the contrary, Dr Jamieson repeatedly stressed, in the reports and in his evidence, that the concentrations found were relatively low. The plaintiffs' case depends on the assumptions as to the occurrence of peak concentrations at fifteen-minute periods at the farm. To make such assumptions where there is no evidence that such peaks actually occurred is to ignore totally the legal burden of proof which rests on the plaintiffs, and this, for the reasons already stated, I am not prepared to do."

The judge went on to say that an instrument for continuous monitoring that would have confirmed or disproved conclusively the existence of such peaks could have been acquired for approximately £5,000. He thought that an insignificant sum in the context of the litigation.

Jamieson himself did not think it particularly likely that the concentrations he had measured as twenty-four hour averages would have arrived at the monitors in short periods; but even more significant, according to Keane, were the predictions of Richard Ruch. These had shown that, given the worst possible weather conditions, the levels of acid and organics arriving at the farm in an hour would have been far too low to damage animal or human life. The judge did not deal with the contradiction between the symptoms reported and the levels recorded, and dismissed the plaintiffs' criticism of the measurement technique. "It also cannot be without significance that there is virtually no evidence in this case of injury to human beings or animals which has been scientifically linked to any chemicals emanating from the defendants' factory."

Dr Rory O'Moore and Professor Ian Temperley had admitted that the minor blood abnormalities detected in the Hanrahan family could have been due to a variety of reasons other than chemical poisoning. Even Fitzgerald could only say it seemed to him that John Hanrahan's respiratory difficulty was linked to some form of atmospheric pollution.

"Most significant of all is the almost total dearth of any clear evidence from the various necropsies carried out on the animals on the Hanrahan farm that they had been subjected to any form of chemical poisoning which could be associated with the factory."

No tests were undertaken for the chemicals used in the Merck factory, and the judge did not appear to be impressed by the testimony of Neufeld, who had come to conclusions markedly different from those of the Department of Agriculture on the condition of the animals slaughtered for post-mortem examination. "In contrast, there is clear evidence to indicate that the undoubted deterioration in the quality of the herd on the Hanrahan farm could have had other explanations."

Necropsies and the evidence of de Lacy himself established that there was hoose on the farm between 1978 and 1983, he said. The coughing observed by the vets who attended the farm was consistent with its proven existence. Equally the sore udders, streaming eyes and nasal discharge were indications of paravaccinia, *Moraxella bovis*, IBR, and IBK.

He accepted the evidence of Lynch and Bielenberg that there was overstocking, too little fertiliser, and poor silage, which, along with hoose, would explain the lack of thrift in the animals. Likewise, the inadequate breeding records could explain the higher twinning rates and deformities; but he thought the evidence did not establish that either brucellosis or mastitis were contributing to the difficulties on the farm.

It had to be borne in mind, the judge said, that the management changed in 1978, when John Hanrahan took over all responsibilities, and this coincided with the start of the problems. "It was singularly unfortunate that these responsibilities, of which he had no previous experience, devolved upon him not long before he and a number of other residents in the area began to experience unpleasant smells clearly emanating from the defendants' factory." He had developed an obsessive belief that the factory was the source of his trouble, and he was therefore unable to give his full attention to the real difficulties on the farm.

In Keane's judgement the overwhelming volume of evidence indicated that the Hanrahan experience was unique. This was established by the evidence of Brendan Walsh and Martin Fitzgerald, who said they had encountered no problems in the area that were not due to well-established causes. Even more remarkable to the judge was the evidence of Dr Michael Carey, showing that the people working in the Merck factory did not have any unusual symptoms of ill health over a long period of years.

"No scientific evidence has been advanced as to why the air pollution alleged by the plaintiffs to emanate from the defendants' factory should so selectively attack the Hanrahan farm, and indeed all the evidence indicates that if the defendants' factory was a source of toxic gases the effects would be felt at other locations, for example Mr and Mrs Perigoe's premises." The Perigoes had made 108 complaints to the factory but they did not give evidence, and the judge had no indication that their complaints were serious enough to warrant medical attention. He therefore dismissed them as affording no support for the case.

The plaintiffs had wholly failed to discharge the onus

of proof upon them, of establishing that the injury to health and to animal and plant life was caused by emissions from the defendants' factory. There was unmistakable evidence that sometimes the factory processes caused offensive odours, which were reasonably objected to by the plaintiffs and others. "I have no doubt that it was the insensitive and cavalier manner in which these well-justified complaints were initially dealt with by the local representatives of the defendants that ultimately led to this litigation."

He had concluded that there was a decline in animal health and mortality from 1978 onwards, that John Hanrahan's health had been damaged, and that plant life on the farm had been damaged, but he did not attribute any of the blame for these phenomena to emissions from Merck, Sharp and Dohme. He dismissed the claim.

□

On 12 November 1985 the Hanrahans' solicitors lodged a notice of appeal to the Supreme Court, citing thirty-seven grounds for appealing Mr Justice Ronan Keane's decision. It said the judge had erred in law and in fact or had misdirected himself on a range of significant issues, and had assessed the evidence as a whole in a way that was unbalanced, unreasonable, or unwarranted.

It was two years before the appeal came up in the Supreme Court. It opened on Monday 30 November 1987 and ran for thirteen days before Chief Justice TA Finlay, Mr Justice Séamus Henchy, and Mr Justice Anthony Hederman.

Opposing counsel outlined the evidence presented in the High Court, emphasising what points they saw fit. The Hanrahans' counsel submitted that the Suir valley was a clean rural area and that the family were entitled to a corresponding standard of comfort, a comfort they had enjoyed before Merck arrived. Satisfaction under the Public Health Acts or under planning controls was not effective, and in trying to restore his rights, the citizen was left with no choice but to go to law.

The Hanrahans' submission argued again that the onus of proof should be shifted to the defendants. The traditional rules on onus of proof were inadequate in this case, because the family were being asked to establish the identity of contaminants produced by the factory when Merck themselves were unable to do so. In fact the contaminants were unknown and unknowable. The judge had underestimated the difficulties of obtaining information from Merck and the disparity in resources.

As might be expected, Merck's submission alluded approvingly to Mr Justice Keane's decision. It cast doubt on the credibility of the Hanrahan family and their principal witnesses, especially Buck, and the vets of de Lacy's practice. They took particular comfort in Jamieson's air quality findings and the theoretical predictions of Ruch showing that the chemical levels at the Hanrahans' farm were low at all times.

During the submissions the judges made a number of interventions that indicated crucial turning-points in their deliberations. Again and again they picked up on the question of hoose. They challenged Merck's senior counsel, Peter Shanley, on his argument that hoose was the main cause of the animal deaths on the farm when so many vets failed to diagnose it, in particular the county council vet, Peter Dougan.

"The nature of his report," Chief Justice Finlay said, "seems to be inconsistent with the condition. He mentions in his report to the county council that there was a problem and he could not say what it was . . . You have here, presumably, a competent and certainly independent vet. He goes to the farm on five separate occasions and he examines a number of animals with respiratory conditions. Hoose is well known, and there does not seem to be any dispute about the concept that it should be easily identifiable. Yet on his own evidence at the very last question, after all this, he reported to the county council that there was a problem and he did not know what it is."

A further critical point appeared to arrive on the tenth

day of the hearing on Mr Justice Keane's High Court conclusion that, although the Hanrahans and others suffered offensive smells from the factory, they were never serious enough to justify an award of damages. "I appreciate he rejected the complaints of ill health," Mr Justice Henchy said, "but what about the smells that affected people short of causing ill health?"

Shanley said that the judge took the view that he could only look at complainants who gave evidence to the court. He was looking, in effect, at the individual Hanrahan complaints.

"If his view is that the complaints made by Mr Hanrahan were legitimate with regard to smell," Chief Justice Finlay asked, ". . . you are, in effect, saying that the judge should be construed as having found that Mr Hanrahan made legitimate complaints about smell but that they weren't as bad as he said? That's what it has come down to?"

"The judge accepts that there was evidence," Shanley answered, and went on to mention the complaints from other people.

The Chief Justice continued: "Do you say that it was open to the judge to accept the nature and frequency of the complaints made in evidence, leaving out the complaints made in evidence by the Hanrahans, and at the same time to hold, properly to hold according to the legal principles, that they did not merit damages?"

"Yes."

"You accept," Mr Justice Hederman suggested later, "that some of the odours that were emanating from your plant in 1978 and 1979 did cause horrendous smells?"

"I wouldn't like to accept that they were—"

"If 'horrendous' is too emotive, extremely objectionable?"

"There is some evidence that the trial judge is entitled to rely on that some of the odours are offensive, certainly."

"Do you accept, Mr Shanley," the Chief Justice asked the following day, "if the learned judge was correct in reaching a conclusion that damages were not awardable, which he did reach—if he was correct as a matter of law in reaching that conclusion, that he must have discounted to a very large extent the complaints of the odours of the three Hanrahans?"

"Yes."

It took the three judges seven months to reach a verdict, and on 5 July 1988 Mr Justice Henchy read it on their behalf.

The verdict accepted the standard of proof required for a case in nuisance as stated by Mr Justice Gannon in *Halpin and Others* v. *Tara Mines*. Either the problems were caused by emissions from the Merck factory or they were not. If, on the balance of probability, they could be said to derive from the factory, the case for nuisance would succeed.

On the onus of proof, what the Hanrahans had to prove was that they suffered some or all of the mischief complained of and that it was caused by the factory emissions. While recognising that there were difficulties in such proof, he said that mere difficulty did not justify shifting the onus from a plaintiff. Neither did the Hanrahans' right to protection of their personal and property rights under the Constitution absolve them of the onus of proof. He held, accordingly, that Mr Justice Keane had correctly rejected the submission that the onus of disproving the allegations rested on Merck.

The kernel of their judgement was the three judges' consideration of what power the appeal court had to interfere with the trial judge's finding of fact. To this end they referred to a statement from the Supreme Court in the case of *J.M. and G.M.* v. *An Bord Uchtála* (1988). That statement made a distinction between primary and secondary facts for purposes of an appeal from the High Court to the Supreme Court. Primary facts were deemed to be those established in the course of oral evidence and accepted by the High Court judge, who had the advantage of seeing and hearing the witnesses presenting them. The Supreme Court would not normally reverse such findings, even where different findings seemed more appropriate.

Secondary facts are derived from the primary facts. Once the primary facts have been established orally, their implications are a matter of deduction. In respect of that deductive process the advantage of the High Court judge is of such minor importance that the Supreme Court would feel free to come up with different secondary facts, to draw its own conclusions.

Mr Justice Henchy noted that most of the primary facts were not in dispute. The real controversy in both the High Court and Supreme Court was whether the factory emissions were the cause of the complaints, as a matter of probability. That was a matter of inference from the primary facts. The appeal would be decided on whether the three judges thought Mr Justice Keane's inference was correct.

The scope of complaints left no doubt in the minds of the trial judge or the appeal court judges that between 1978 and 1983 the Hanrahans and their animals suffered ill health, distress and death and that there was unusual damage to plants. The point at issue for the Supreme Court was whether Keane was correct in finding that the factory was not the common cause of these complaints. It became a matter of whether to believe the evidence of witnesses whose truthfulness was not in question or the largely abstract evidence of scientists who had no direct or personal experience of the matters complained of.

Having established the legal context, Henchy turned to their decisions. Dealing first with the question of smells, he pointed to Keane's opinion that, though the evidence showed beyond doubt that the factory processes caused occasional offensive odours, they were not of such intensity as to justify an award of damages. "This conclusion seems to me to be incorrect," Henchy said, "not so much as an inference drawn from the facts as a misrepresentation of the relevant law."

It was the first chink of light for the Hanrahans. The judge went on to outline the test for nuisance: whether the reasonable person should have to put up with the smell; it was not necessary to show damage to health. "I would hold that each of the three plaintiffs has made out a case for damages for nuisance caused by offensive smells from the defendants' factory."

Next he considered the question of John Hanrahan's health, against the background of the general evidence of factory emissions. The evidence seemed to show beyond doubt that atmospheric pollution in the neighbouring farms was caused by emissions from the factory, even if only the Hanrahans claimed that it affected their health.

There was largely uncontroverted evidence from people in the area of burning sensation in the throat and chest, reddening of the skin, irritation and streaming of the eyes, and a smothering feeling in the nose, throat, and chest. "Whether or not the Hanrahan farm vis-à-vis the factory was in a special meteorological position, there was unimpeached independent evidence that the complaints of physical ill effects in humans on the plaintiffs' farm were matched by observable distress in the animals on the farm."

In fact the trial judge had held that the evidence established human and animal ill health and unusual plant damage on the farm in the relevant period. "The only real question, therefore, is whether the judge's finding of no causal connection between those complaints and emissions from the factory can be sustained."

Different witnesses described seeing clouds of emissions coming from the factory and at the same time feeling discomfort and distress, observing decay in plants, noticing animals coughing and lowing, and later finding unexplained abnormalities in the herd. Coupled with such evidence were the defendants' admissions that the emissions gave offence. "There were uncontroverted items of complaints which suggested that the factory emissions were at the root of the trouble."

John Hanrahan had given evidence specifically of suffering from wheezing and chest pains after seeing clouds of emissions from the factory and having burning sensations on his skin and eyes and blisters on his tongue and head.

His general practitioner had referred him to Professor Fitzgerald, who found he was suffering from wheezing and pulmonary obstruction. Blood tests had shown him to be suffering from hyperchloraemic acidosis and a mild decrease in white cell count, consistent with solvent poisoning.

Henchy quoted Fitzgerald's uncontroverted and carefully worded opinion that, on the balance of probabilities, Hanrahan's lung disease was caused by toxic emissions from the factory, because that was the only local source of toxic substances. The High Court judge had said that the value of Fitzgerald's opinion was significantly reduced by the unexplained absence of evidence from the general practitioner or corroborating evidence from the rest of the family. "I am of the opinion that the judge's ruling was incorrect and was not supported by the evidence." It was likely that Fitzgerald had given his opinion knowing that the rest of the family had not shown the same symptoms, and it could not be assumed that the general practitioner's evidence would have weakened Fitzgerald's opinion if it had been available. By December 1984 the atmospheric pollution from the factory had abated, and Merck's consultant physician found Hanrahan's chest condition to be normal. That indicated that he was not suffering from any long-standing lung disorder.

"I would hold," Henchy concluded, "that John Hanrahan is entitled to damages for the ill health he suffered as a result of the nuisance caused by the factory emissions."

Mary Hanrahan had not been able to say in the witness box what ill health she was blaming on the factory. She said her doctor would know, but no doctor was called to testify, and Henchy concluded that the trial judge's rejection of her claim for ill health could not be disturbed.

Considering the gynaecological nature of Selina Hanrahan's complaints and the fact that there was no medical evidence to connect these with the factory emissions, it was not surprising, Henchy said, that the trial judge had rejected her claim, apparently disregarding the evidence of blood disorders in her case.

Mr Justice Keane had not specifically rejected the evidence of damage to plant life, but it was implicit in his judgement that he thought a case for damages had not been proved. The evidence of damage to plant life lent support to other complaints, Henchy said, but he found it did not warrant a separate award of damages for nuisance.

The Supreme Court judges next considered the ill effects suffered by the Hanrahans' dairy herd from the factory emissions. Henchy said there appeared to be little doubt that the Merck factory was the main source of hydrogen chloride and hydrochloric acid mists in the Suir valley. The scientific evidence as a whole, including Jamieson's air quality measurements, led him to the conclusion that it only showed what could or should have happened by way of toxic damage. In the light of what did happen, such evidence should not be allowed to prevail. Proven facts were that John Hanrahan suffered ill health as a result of toxic emissions from the factory; there was unusual damage to plant life on the farm; and there was a volume of eyewitness accounts that animals were seen and heard to be ill and in distress at a time when the observer was getting foul chemical smells or weeping eyes or irritated skin which could only have been caused by the factory.

"It would be to allow scientific theorising to dethrone fact to dispose of this claim by saying, as was said in the judgement under appeal, that there was virtually no evidence in this case of injury to human beings or animals which has been scientifically linked to any chemicals emanating from the defendants' factory." The main factors supporting the conclusion that the animal ill health was caused by the factory emissions were that the herd was thriving up to the time the emissions were detected; the firm opinion of the five vets who regularly treated the animals that their ailments were caused by toxic emissions; the fact that the factory incinerator was run for long periods at temperatures too low to destroy the chemical solvents it was burning, making damage to humans and animals highly likely; and that the conditions suffered by the cattle were too pronounced and varied to be accounted for by natural causes or bad management. The most credible explanation offered for the ailments and abnormalities was the toxic emissions from the factory.

Henchy looked up from his judgement and scanned the court. "I would therefore allow the appeal against the finding that the plaintiffs had not established as a matter of probability that the complaints about the condition of the cattle were not causally linked to toxic emissions from the defendants' factory."

What should have been the issue at the trial, he said, was whether the animal ailments were due entirely to the factory emissions or whether factors like hoose or bad management were contributory. Keane had made no finding on this question, because he discounted the factory emissions as a cause of the plaintiffs' complaints. Though accepting the Hanrahans' case, Henchy and his colleagues decided it would not be proper for them to quantify the factory's responsibility for the cattle problems and to assess damages; there would have to be another High Court hearing for that.

In summary, the judges decided that Merck, Sharp and Dohme were liable to the Hanrahans for damages for offensive smells, for injury to John Hanrahan's health, and for the cattle ailments in so far as they were caused by factory emissions. They sent the case back for the High Court to decide the extent of Merck's liability for cattle ailments and to assess total damages.

In the body of the court a degree of caution tempered the Hanrahans' jubilation, as if, knowing they had won, they were almost afraid to believe it. What did it mean? Could they afford to fight another case? Could the High Court again decide against them? Gleeson, Smyth and Menton were all now assuring them they had won. Merck would have to pay all costs, including those of the next case, which would merely decide the size of their award.

The Supreme Court was now reflecting almost a mirror image of the scenes in courtroom number 1 three years earlier. The press crowded around the Hanrahans as the Merck team began to file out in glum silence. "It's like as if a huge cloud has lifted from my shoulders," John Hanrahan was telling reporters as they made their way outside. "Like as if the whole family was free again. There can be no more cover-ups."

The Hanrahans' ten-year attempt to prove their case was already assuming the epic proportions of a David and Goliath struggle. Henchy's judgement was dubbed a watershed, a landmark decision that would have long-term repercussions on the chemical industry in Ireland and indeed elsewhere.

But the loss of their herd, the cost in health, stress, anxiety, the emotional costs to the Hanrahans, were yet to be counted. In fact it would be a further two-and-a-half years before they got a penny for their pains.

15

PARALLELS

The first blind calf was nothing to worry about. He found it one early spring morning, staggering about the calving pen with a more than usually uncertain gait for a newborn. Later there were more blind calves, some one-eyed, some small and weak or with other deformities. Some cows aborted, and almost all the births were difficult, and he had his first adult deaths. Others he sold for slaughter at a fraction of their value.

"The hardest part was going out in the morning, seeing all the cows there, wasting, and the little calves so weak— it was terrible."

This was not John Hanrahan speaking but Andrew Graham, who kept a dairy herd at Milngavie, just north of Glasgow. Like John Hanrahan he had acquired a reputation for one of the best-managed and highest-yielding herds in his area.

Towards the middle of April 1980 he sent half the herd to graze on his father-in-law's farm at Bankhead, twenty miles to the north-east. Less than two miles below the farm is the small town of Bonnybridge in the Forth valley, and towering above the town the 200-foot stack of a toxic waste incinerator owned by Rechem International. When the east wind blew in off the Firth of Forth it carried the incinerator emissions straight towards the Bankhead farm on the side of the valley.

Graham began to blame these emissions for his

problems. He knew that Rechem was burning polychlorinated biphenyls (PCBs), notorious as a cause of environmental pollution. PCBs were widely used as a coating for
electrical transformers and in lubricants, paints, plastics,
and printing inks; their manufacture has now been stopped,
but thousands of tonnes remain to be disposed of. To
destroy them by incineration a flame temperature of 1,000
degrees Celsius or more is required at all times; at cooler
temperatures the products of incomplete combustion may
include unburnt PCBs as well as dioxins and furans.
Residents in the Bonnybridge area had reported seeing
clouds of black smoke from the stack, suggesting that
combustion was incomplete. Company officials repeatedly
denied any links between local health problems and their
plant.

Apart from deaths and deformities, Graham claimed to
have identified twenty-five different disorders in his herd,
including hair loss, running eyes, listless appearance, wild
and aggressive behaviour before calving, swollen joints,
reproductive disorders, and lung problems. By 1984 he had
lost 112 cows and 68 calves, and the annual milk yield had
fallen from 1,000 to 350 gallons per cow. The remaining
animals were in such poor condition that he had lost faith
in their prospects of survival. They would have to go.

Inevitably came the studies. The first, carried out by
Glasgow Veterinary School, diagnosed "fat cow syndrome,"
sometimes known as "fatty liver," caused by overfeeding
an unbalanced diet. It found no evidence of pollution.

In January 1984 the British government released the
results of investigations by the Industrial Pollution
Inspectorate. Continuous air sampling since 1982 had found
no evidence of exceptional levels of metals in the air around
the incinerator. Discharges to the atmosphere had been
analysed for dust, grit, and PCBs, and found to be of low
environmental significance. Soil, grass and straw samples
from the Bankhead farm were tested for zinc, lead, copper,
cadmium, and aluminium, and no differences from normal
locations were found. The report also stated that the

Inspectorate routinely examined the company's record of incinerator temperatures; had they done so on 28 May 1984 they would have noted an entry in Rechem's log showing that the temperature had dropped to 800 degrees in one of the cells. There were further references to temperatures falling to 800 and 825 degrees on two days in June 1984 and at other times.

Twenty-eight farms in Stirlingshire were inspected in 1983, ten of them in the vicinity of Graham's Bankhead farm. All had suffered losses; but the official report attributed these to well-known diseases or husbandry shortcomings. Graham found the suggestion of bad farm management no less infuriating than John Hanrahan did in South Tipperary.

Like Hanrahan, Graham engaged his own specialists. An American toxicologist who had worked on similar cases sent soil and animal samples to a Canadian laboratory for analysis. The results showed that detectable levels of dioxins and furans had been found in some samples; the toxicologist said he was convinced they were escaping in emissions from the incinerator.

In the summer of 1984 a number of babies were born in the Stirlingshire area with microphthalmos (small eye syndrome)—similar to defects observed in Graham's calves—and the government decided to set up an independent public inquiry. This reported in February 1985 that there was no link between the plant and the problems in children and cattle, but that there was need for further investigations and for a nationwide programme to discover the effects of toxic waste.

In the meantime workers at the plant had refused to incinerate any more PCBs, and in October 1984 Rechem decided to close it. The company continued to insist that the plant had been safely operated and that the closure had been "for entirely financial reasons."

Close to bankruptcy, Andrew Graham had his entire herd slaughtered in 1987, and he is now suing Rechem for damages. Unlike his Irish counterpart, however, Graham has been granted free legal aid to fight the case.

Joining Andrew Graham in his action against Rechem is Colin Haines, a beef and sheep farmer from a valley near Pontypool in Gwent, Wales, where Rechem operates another toxic waste incinerator. He claims to have lost as many as three hundred animals during 1983 and 1984 because of toxic emissions. "They suffer from appalling sores and flesh dropping off, loss of condition, lack of growth, stiff limbs and finally pneumonia before they die of starvation." Other local farmers reported similar symptoms.

An official inquiry in 1985 concluded that the conditions were not linked to the factory; but reports of human symptoms prompted further studies. Aching limbs, nosebleeds, running eyes and noses, sore throats, foul tastes and smells, dizziness and general malaise were common in the village of New Inn beside the plant. The village was sometimes shrouded in emissions, and the residents began to collect a fighting fund to take the company to court. It became known that between 1980 and 1984 at least four babies were born with rare eye defects within ten miles of the plant. These were thought to be the small eye syndrome reported previously from Bonnybridge. The government admitted that the incidence of deformed babies in the area had been higher since the plant opened in 1974 than in the rest of Gwent. But the study did not suggest that Rechem was in any way responsible; nor did a further study by consultants in February 1985, nor an official study on dioxins and furans in 1989.

Traces of dioxin were found near New Inn in 1984. In 1989 the government confirmed that analyses showed relatively high levels of PCBs in soil, grass and duck eggs from the vicinity of the plant. But parallel tests done by Rechem showed much lower levels, and they say the PCBs did not come from the plant but from flooding by the local river. A company spokesman said PCBs are "ubiquitous" in the environment and quoted a University of Wales study showing PCB levels eighteen times higher in eggs of Welsh river birds.

In 1989 Torfaen District Council threatened to sue

en the company cast doubt on the
tests showing that PCB levels in foliage
plant were up to eighty-eight times higher
ground levels. Rechem retaliated with an
stopping the council from publishing the results
erate pressure for a public inquiry. The injunction
is lifted a month later.

Finally, in August 1990 the British government ordered an independent inquiry under the supervision of Professor Lewis Roberts of the University of East Anglia. The outcome is awaited.

Battle Creek, Michigan, was the scene of perhaps the most celebrated toxic poisoning of farm animals. Unlike the foregoing cases, it did not involve an incinerator or airborne toxic emissions. It began in late September 1973 when a dairy farmer noticed a dramatic drop in milk production from his 400-cow herd. Within three weeks the daily output of the herd had fallen by half, while at the same time the cows were visibly wasting. As they lost weight and milk production, they developed running eyes, sore feet, shrunken udders, hair loss, and reproductive disorders. Deaths and deformities followed at an alarming rate. Vets were at a loss to explain the developments, and laboratory tests carried out by Michigan Department of Agriculture showed nothing they thought was abnormal. It was suggested that husbandry practices were at fault.

Finally, in April 1974, it was discovered that polybrominated biphenyl (PBB), a close relative of PCB, had been added by mistake to a Michigan company's cattle feed and had found its way to the Battle Creek farm. By July 1974 more than thirty Michigan dairy herds and 100 animal feed plants were quarantined, and several thousand animals were slaughtered eventually. But in the meantime, contaminated milk and meat had found its way into the food chain of Michigan's nine million people. After several years the Battle Creek farmer lost his law suit for damages against the chemical company.

These case histories show a striking similarity with the

Hanrahan story. In particular it is remarkable how close were the parallels in official approach as the problems developed, in the suggestion that the farmer was the author of his own misfortune, or a crank. They showed a disturbing readiness to accept the results of initial tests that found no link between farm and factory, a reluctance to believe that the chemical companies may have been at least partly to blame. It required exceptional perseverance and expense from the farmers to establish the merits of their cases.

☐

On 14 July 1989 the Dutch government banned the sales of milk and meat from sixteen farms because they were found to be contaminated with dioxin. The farms, with an annual milk output of about one million gallons, are in the area surrounding two large incinerators at the Rijmond waste disposal centre near Rotterdam.

☐

In the Jaiprakash Nagar shanty district of Bhopal, India, stands a large stone figure of a woman in pain, face skewed to heaven, mouth open, gasping, one hand covering her eyes. Across the dirt road is the closed and now overgrown Union Carbide chemical factory that made Bhopal a by-word for disaster. The stone figure is a monument to those who died when, just after midnight on 3 December 1984, a stream of toxic gas began to escape from the factory. The factory is a monument, too, to the chemical industry's capacity for catastrophe.

Within an hour of the escape a heavy cloud of methyl isocyanate (MIC) had spread through the city's slums, suffocating 2,000 people in their beds, causing irreversible lung damage to many who survived for a time, and blinding thousands more. As many as 10,000 may have died eventually, and 200,000 more suffered severe damage to eyes, lungs, liver, kidney, and nervous system. There is a legacy of birth defects, deformities, and reproductive diseases. It was a chemical Hiroshima.

What caused the accident was water seeping into underground storage tanks and reacting with MIC. The resulting build-up of pressure drove about 45 tonnes of gas and liquid chemicals past the safety systems and scrubbers and out into the atmosphere. There were similar accidents on a smaller scale at the Merck plant in Ballydine a number of times when hydrochloric acid overwhelmed the scrubber system and escaped.

In Charleston, West Virginia, where Union Carbide has another MIC factory, the company's response was to close down for four months and spend 5 million dollars in safety alterations and a computerised alarm system. After inspectors gave the plant a clean bill of health Union Carbide's chairman, Warren Anderson, wrote a letter of assurance to a local teacher. "We have taken steps to ensure that this already safe facility has been made even safer." But on the morning of 11 August 1985 the Bhopal accident was replicated in the Charleston plant, although without the tragedy. Two chemicals came together and caused a runaway reaction that overwhelmed the safety systems and blew a heavy toxic gas out of the plant. This time in daylight observers saw a white crescent-shaped cloud forming near the ground and slowly moving towards the nearby West Virginia College. There was time to raise the alarm, and most of the community was evacuated, although 135 people needed treatment in hospital.

Afterwards the company was accused of a cover-up as in Bhopal and of failing to disclose the exact nature of the toxic gas. Whatever the merits of those charges, the West Virginia accident left the chemical industry's assurances about safety sounding rather hollow.

☐

For another American chemical company, Merrell Dow, the timing of the Hanrahan case was unfortunate. Ten

days after the Supreme Court decision the company applied
to Cork County Council for permission to build a factory
at Killeagh, twenty-five miles east of Cork. Planning
permission was granted on 26 August 1988.

The site chosen was a three-mile-wide plain between
the south coast and a line of low hills to the north. Running
due east through this fertile farmland is the Womanagh
River, entering the sea at Youghal five miles away. The
river is tidal at the point where up to 100,000 gallons a day
of treated factory effluent would join it, and the land is
subject to periodic flooding.

More than a thousand dairy cows are kept in the
surrounding farmland by some two dozen farmers who
became part of the Womanagh Valley Protection Association. This group objected to the proposal, along with the
Youghal Fishermen's Association, Youghal Urban District
Council, the Southern Fisheries Board, the regional tourism
organisation, and others.

Youghal is a popular tourist resort, but it is also an
unemployment black-spot. The project would provide 300
jobs during construction, leaving an estimated £15 million
in the community. When the plant began operations there
would be ninety full-time jobs, with a promise of 200 more
jobs in the long term.

According to Merrell Dow's account they chose Ireland
because they were invited by the IDA to examine Irish
locations. "The company . . . was impressed by the
availability of an educated, English-speaking work force,
the stable political environment for business, and the
package of financial incentives in terms of tax incentives
and grants." What they might also have said was that they
wanted a rural site to give a fresh, wholesome image to
their product. They rejected the IDA's encouragement to
locate in the Cork Harbour area, which already has a colony
of chemical plants—and an uneasy relationship with the
local community.

Most of the plant effluent would come from the chemical
waste incinerator, fitted with a scrubber. The effluent would

be neutralised in a biological treatment plant before discharge to the Womanagh river at ebbing tide. There would be small emissions of hydrogen chloride and carbon dioxide from the process building. A ninety-foot boiler stack would vent sulphur dioxide, and the incinerator would emit the by-products of burning organic wastes. To the lay person it was a replica of Ballydine, and as the opposition gathered momentum, attention was increasingly drawn to the experience there.

Cork County Council had laid down much tighter conditions than those applying in South Tipperary, especially for the incinerator; but the opposition was not convinced, and appealed to An Bord Pleanála. They distrusted the council's ability to enforce the emission standards, and wondered what would happen if the effluent treatment system or the incinerator scrubber went wrong, as it had at Ballydine and elsewhere.

An Bord Pleanála upheld the council's decision to grant planning permission. But the WVPA would not be thwarted, and four of its farmer-members sought a judicial review of the decision in the High Court. On 27 July 1989 Mr Justice Barron decided that the planning application was valid, and he rejected the application.

But public opposition to the project appeared to be widening. After the general election of 1989 the WVPA invited elected representatives to view the site, and the new Minister of State for the Environment, Mary Harney, visited Killeagh. She told the objectors there would be no direct Government intervention, but on 24 August she and Desmond O'Malley met senior Merrell Dow executives. They apparently asked them to postpone any development until the proposed Environmental Protection Agency had been set up.

The Merrell Dow decision to cancel the project was unexpected. It came on 4 September, when they announced that plans to build the Killeagh plant had been abandoned because a merger with another American company made it unnecessary. According to an *Irish Times* report the following day the company told the IDA that, following the merger, Ireland's 10 per cent corporate tax rate no longer offered significant financial advantages. If they were seeking sites for new factories in Europe in future Ireland would be on the list. However, they added, "Killeagh would not."

☐

In the early summer of 1989, while the Merrell Dow case was still undecided, rumours began to circulate that a chemical company was about to set up a plant in Cork Harbour. By early July the IDA had confirmed that the Sandoz company of Switzerland wanted to build a £170 million plant at Ringaskiddy and were inviting community groups, politicians, business people, trade unionists and the media to discuss their plans. This was a new departure by the IDA and a marked contrast to the approach in the Merrell Dow case, where the company had first obtained planning permission and then tried to sell the idea to the community.

Later, following the Merrell Dow withdrawal, the Minister for Industry and Commerce, Desmond O'Malley, drew a distinction between the Merrell Dow case and the Sandoz proposal. Ringaskiddy was an industrial estate especially developed for industry, he said, and the proposal was fully supported by the Government. Eventually the project got planning permission from Cork County Council in December 1989, subject to seventy conditions. The decision was appealed by a number of groups under the umbrella of Cork Environmental Alliance; in July An Bord Pleanála upheld the council decision, subject to a further twenty-eight conditions—the strictest so far imposed on a chemical plant—and building began.

During the Sandoz controversy, Cork County Council brought prosecutions for violation of air pollution regulations against Penn Chemicals and Angus Fines, two chemical companies in Cork Harbour. They were the first such prosecutions in the country. The success of the new enforcement policy of Cork County Council has yet to be judged, but it is at least an advance on the kind of benevolent indulgence that had previously passed for a strategy. For more than fifteen years the residents of Cork Harbour had to tolerate foul odours as their protests were largely ignored. The residents of South Tipperary suffered likewise, but far from prosecution, Merck, Sharp and Dohme were allowed to operate without regular monitoring, and even when the company admitted substantially exceeding its planning limits for both air and water, there were no repercussions.

Cork Environmental Alliance may have lost the battle to stop Sandoz but they have probably won the war. In future it is difficult to imagine any chemical projects getting past the praetorian guard of environmentalists without the most thorough inquisition. How they behave once inside the gate depends largely on whether the proposed Environmental Protection Agency is given the powers to enforce the conditions attached to planning permissions. Experience has shown that local authorities have not got the skill, the equipment, the money or indeed the independence to do so.

16

A PARABLE OF OUR TIME

Following the Supreme Court decision, the Hanrahan team set about preparing for the new High Court case to assess damages. An early hearing was expected, and it was comforting to know that all costs were covered and that some award of damages was guaranteed.

They reckoned without the resilience of Merck, Sharp and Dohme. The company made a lodgement to the court, a figure in the region of £500,000. The Hanrahans could either accept this or decide to fight the case hoping for more; but if they rejected the money and the court awarded them less than £500,000, the family stood to lose again. Costs of another protracted session in court could amount to a million pounds or more, and they would have to pay the difference between those costs and the award. The pressure was back on the Hanrahans.

They knew also that £500,000 would leave very little to show for the trauma of the ten-year battle. Most of that sum was already owed to the banks and Avonmore Co-op, and there was the lasting physical and mental health damage that could still lead to untold expense. True to form, the Hanrahans decided to fight.

Further expertise was employed to assess the extent of compensatable losses: the nuisance to all the family, the damage to human and animal health, and production losses due to the factory emissions. An additional factor was the income and production lost at the critical time when milk quotas were introduced (whereby dairy farms were restricted to producing the volume of milk they had sold in the year beginning 1 April 1983): had the herd expanded at the expected rate, they argued, the farm would have reached a much higher production level in 1983 than it actually did.

Preparations were protracted, including consultation with up to a dozen specialists who would testify to the damage done to human health and several more who would deal with animal health and farming losses. In addition, some test results came to hand that were not available at the time of the first High Court hearing.

In the autumn of 1990, more than two years after the Supreme Court verdict, the Hanrahans put in a claim against Merck for £1.8 million, not including damages for health and stress. The High Court hearing was set for February 1991. Merck's response was to make a further lodgement and to invite the Hanrahans to accept an out-of-court settlement. After further negotiations between the legal teams over costs, agreement was reached in late November 1990. The settlement figure has not been made public, but indications are that it was somewhere between Merck's original lodgement of £500,000 and the Hanrahans' claim. At that it would be reasonable financial compensation for the family's effort. Including all legal and other expenses, the total cost to Merck cannot have been less than £5 million.

But the real cost is incalculable. These days John Hanrahan's general health is reasonably good for a man in his early forties, but he gets intermittent recurrence of wheezing in his chest, which can last for weeks at a time; nobody knows whether or at what rate the condition could develop as he gets older. One apparently irreversible symptom is the loss of reflexes and co-ordination in his limbs.

The Supreme Court verdict did not link Selina's gynaecological problems with the Merck operation, but by coincidence she, like her husband, endures long bouts of flu-like symptoms, weakness, pains, and sensations in her limbs. She is often stressed, and feels acutely what she regards as the loss of twelve of the most important years of her life. Over the years she has taken the brunt of the mental buffeting and uncertainty of the whole episode. Had the final High Court case gone to a hearing, the family had accumulated a body of specialist evidence towards a claim for further damages on this count.

Mary Hanrahan is going strong at seventy-three, still unable to describe her physical ailments, no more than she was in court. But people of her experience and doughty attitude to life are slow to complain. Though the whole affair must have hurt, she has refused to let it show.

Charles and Ambrose have survived with all the resilience of youth. They are young men now, grown up perhaps more quickly than a child psychologist would have wished. Who is to say what the legacy will be for them or indeed the rest of the family? But the indications are that their lives are getting back to normal. Charles and Ambrose are again living in Ballycurkeen and, with some trepidation, John and Selina are contemplating a move back also.

And what of the farm? After the auction in the autumn of 1985 John Hanrahan was left with about a third of his stock. The auction money went to pay some outstanding legal costs and towards fighting the Supreme Court case. The family's credit was all used up, so the farm was left to fund any redevelopment itself. By far the most valuable asset was a milk quota of 150,000 gallons; by the early summer of 1991 Hanrahan was filling his quota, and stock numbers on the farm were back to the peak they had reached in the early eighties. In fact the farm has seen "a very rapid build-up in cow numbers during the last six years"—40 per cent a year, not 40 per cent over the whole six-year period, considered by the Lynch report to be putting undue managerial strain on Hanrahan. The animals are not dying. They have no hoose, no pneumonia, no respiratory distress. They do not suffer from loss of condition, lack of thrift, or reduced milk yield. Nor do they have weeping eyes, running noses, hair loss, sore teats, dropping of the cud, stampeding, or overgrown hooves. Hanrahan's farm is not overstocked or underfertilised, and the animals are not underfed.

However, there are some lingering symptoms of the Merck era. There is the odd stillbirth, the odd deformity, and some cows are still showing hormone imbalance. Now and then they get a cloud of irritating gas that burns the eyes, and occasional offensive odours, but the Hanrahans made only two of the fifteen complaints to the factory in the twelve months ending June 1989.

☐

On 1 February 1989, with the High Court case still pending, the Hanrahans' solicitor, Tom Menton, wrote to South Tipperary County Council asking whether Merck, Sharp and Dohme had applied for an operating licence under the Air Pollution Act, 1987. The law said that industrial plants like Merck would not be allowed to operate without a licence under the Act after 1 March 1989. Menton got no reply to his letter; but on the last day of February the company applied to the council for a licence to operate broadly in accordance with the conditions already laid down in the planning permission. He kept on posting enquiries until finally the licence was granted twenty-two months later on 10 December 1990.

On 7 January 1991 Menton lodged an appeal on the Hanrahans' behalf with An Bord Pleanála against the council's decision to grant the operating licence. The grounds for appeal were that the three-year period being allowed to the company to comply with the new regulations was excessive; that the company was not being asked to fit a scrubber to the incinerator; that the waste material would not be in the fire long enough for complete combustion; and that the arrangements for monitoring the factory emissions were inadequate.

A request for an oral hearing was rejected, and on 26 August 1991 An Bord Pleanála decided to grant the licence with stricter conditions, taking account of the Hanrahans' objections.

The three-year period for complying with the strictest of the new conditions was cut to eighteen months, and closer monitoring will apply. For the scrubber stack the new limit for hydrochloric acid emissions, the source of much trouble to the Hanrahans, will be only 7 per cent of the old limit. For the first time there will be separate limits on emissions of individual organic chemicals like toluene, chloroform, and monochlorobenzene, depending on their toxicity, at tiny proportions of their previous limits.

For the incinerator, organic emissions are to be only 2 per cent of the old allowance and hydrochloric acid emissions only 10 per cent, and chlorine will be allowed in the feed tank also at only 10 per cent of the previous recommendation. The tank contents will have to meet the council's approval each time before a burn can begin.

In addition the licence lays down strict conditions to prevent a recurrence of low-temperature operation of the incinerator. The minimum burning temperature is set at 800 degrees Celsius, and the machine will need a system of recording temperatures and measuring feed flow, and automatic cut-off when the temperature drops. Monitoring of stack emissions must be continuous during operation, and the council must set up a system for measuring the air in the countryside around the plant to ensure that chemical levels remain unchanged. However, the new incinerator conditions will not apply for twelve months after the licence comes into operation.

Finally, in future Merck will have to pay the cost of all monitoring, including that undertaken by the county council for air quality.

Most of the new conditions demanded by An Bord Pleanála were recommended by the Hanrahans' adviser, Dr Paul Dowding of TCD. Only his recommendation that a scrubbing device be fitted to the incinerator and that the stack should be raised were not adopted.

By and large, the conditions set in the new licence are

a vindication of the stance adopted by the Hanrahans. It must be assumed that those applying since Merck began operations at Ballydine are now considered excessive and dangerous: had the new limits applied in the early eighties, during the period of the Hanrahans' worst complaints, they would have been exceeded repeatedly. It must be assumed also that the more lenient conditions South Tipperary County Council was prepared to grant in the new licence would have been allowed to stand had the Hanrahans not objected yet again.

So the fight goes on. The Hanrahans have discovered that the price of free air, no less than freedom itself, would appear to be eternal vigilance.

Monetary compensation aside, it is unlikely that the debt owed by society to the Hanrahans will ever be paid. What is the price of showing that ordinary citizens can successfully challenge the might of a multinational?

It is a tribute to the competence of the judicial system that the longest and one of the most complex civil cases in Irish legal history could be concluded satisfactorily. But that the family itself should have to put so much at stake to do so, without state legal aid, is surely an indictment of the same system.

More than a dozen official reports on the Ballydine problem were unable to show that Merck, Sharp and Dohme were in breach of their planning permission, although one report did mention it in passing. No emission records whatever were reported to the county council until the end of 1981. By then it was too late. Neither had the council made any attempt to force the company to comply with the monitoring obligations of its permit.

Despite two technical studies, it took a court order and forty-seven days in the High Court to uncover the full extent of malfunction in the incinerator. It took three years and a further fourteen days in the Supreme Court before these facts were accepted. The same legal recourse and the extraordinary, even obsessive, persistence of the family was required to prove that Merck emissions must have been reaching the Hanrahan farm in dangerous amounts. The combined wisdom of science and Government was unable to establish it.

Referring to the Hanrahan case in his recent auto-biography, *All in a Life*, the former Taoiseach, Dr Garret FitzGerald, put this failure in context. "It was disturbing that the farmer won his case partly on grounds of facts ... that directly and flatly contradicted what I had been told by the officials whom I had asked to examine the matter." He was concerned at the time lest the officials' commitment to industrial promotion and the reputation of the country's farm exports was clouding their judgement.

Equally disturbing is the failure to fully allay suspicions raised by Dr FitzGerald in July 1983 and elsewhere that chemical pollution in the Ballydine valley might be linked to human illness and death. A report of a limited epidemiological study by the county medical officer of health undertaken in 1983 has not been published, although he has said no unusual trends were evident.

Dr Muiris Fitzgerald, professor of medicine at UCD, addressed the need for continuing vigilance in Ballydine. "If materials like solvents are being chronically deposited in the environment," he said, "you may have to wait many years before certain known side-effects of those materials manifest themselves. For example, leukaemias related to benzenes or solvents may not appear for many years. So clearly it is important that there is intensive, sophisticated, on-going monitoring of that area." If continuous monitoring had been undertaken it might have been able to determine whether accounts of premature death from cancer, heart attack and other ailments in the Ballydine area in recent years have any significance. These deaths may be entirely independent of atmospheric pollution, but in the light of the Hanrahan experience it would be unusual if the possibility of such links did not arise in the public mind.

☐

Controlling the chemical industry is not the biggest problem facing an island that young people have been leaving for 150 years because it cannot support them. But it can be no solution to unemployment to allow the chemical industry to hold us to ransom because of a desperate need for the jobs it provides.

Over the last twenty-five years Governments have pursued a two-pronged economic strategy, on the one hand fostering the country's image as a source of high-quality food and on the other hand promoting industrial development by attracting foreign investment.

The Hanrahan case has raised serious doubts whether the two prongs of this strategy are compatible, whether so small an island can support a reputation for high-quality food and maintain at the same time a vigorous chemical industry. When that conflict of interests was exposed in Ballydine, the official response did little to suggest it could be resolved.

Hanrahan is already a household name with Irish environmental organisations, from the Cork Environmental Alliance to the group opposing the Du Pont incinerator proposal in Derry. Through the efforts of Greenpeace, it is increasingly familiar also to the international watchdog fraternity. In a more tangible way the outcome of the case has already had a crucial bearing on the Merrell Dow and Sandoz controversies, the situation in Cork Harbour, and the establishment of the Environmental Protection Agency. In the chronicle of the Irish chemical industry there is little doubt that the Hanrahan case will be seen as a turning-point, in alerting the public to the dangers of chemical manufacturing.

Today the products of organic chemistry are essential to what we have chosen to describe as the civilised world. They are part and parcel of our food, our clothes, our houses, our cars. They may be a more essential part of what we have come to demand but do not absolutely need, things it is convenient to have, like pesticides, herbicides, the ubiquitous plastics, the drugs that keep our anxiety down. Many of these products have a light, comfortable feel about them, a nice clinical appearance, an affordable price tag. Chemical factories have none of the ugly black smokestacks, the depressing aura of heavy industry. They are clean and bright and landscaped.

But in reality organic chemical manufacture is a dirty, dangerous business that comes at a high price. Its by-products go into hazardous waste land-fills, into toxic waste-water. They go up into the air as benzene, toluene, monochlorobenzene, chloroform, PCBs, furans, and dioxins; they come down as lung cancer in New York, bladder cancer in New Jersey, a brain tumour in Michigan, a cleft palate in Illinois, bronchitis in Bhopal, a child with small eyes in Bonnybridge, a poisoned duck egg in Pontypool, a calf with no head in South Tipperary.

It is well known that unbridled use of organic chemicals carries a high price, but the forces promoting indulgence of the industry are far stronger, wealthier and better organised than those advocating restraint. But already there are signs that the price paid by the Hanrahans may not have been in vain. We may have begun to see that what happened to them is no more than a graphic example of what our life-style is doing to us quietly, a parable of our time.

INDEX